GW01046564

Petroleum Exploration Society *of Great Britain*

The Society (PESGB) was set up in 1964. It is a registered charity and a non-profit making organisation, with a membership of some 4000 Active (individual) members and around 60 Sustaining (company) members.

The Executive Committee runs the Society on a voluntary basis, and is elected yearly from the Membership. The object of the Society is to promote, for the public benefit, education in the scientific and technical aspects of petroleum exploration.

Monthly meetings are held in London and Aberdeen. Occasional Conferences and Seminars are organised such as the regular PETEX Shows. The Society also runs several field trips throughout the year.

Further information about the PESGB is available from Karen Whitehead at the PESGB Offices.

Published by
Petroleum Exploration Society
of Great Britain
2nd *Floor*
17/18 *Dover Street*
London *W1X 3PB*
Telephone *0171* 495 6800
Facsimile *0171* 495 7808
E-Mail *pesgb*@pesgb.demon.co.uk.
Registered Charity No **296931**

Designed, Produced and Printed by
Draftoil
6 Dorset Street
London WIH 3FE
Telephone 0171 935 3741
Facsimile 0171 935 3795
E-Mail 100103.1744@compuserve.com
Diskfax 0171 935 3795

First published 1995

©1995 **Petroleum Exploration Society** *of Great Britain*

British Library Cataloguing in Publication Data.
A catalogue record for this book is available from the British Library.

ISBN 0 9527044 0 4

Cover (and over page) The dawn for North Sea Oil. The Ocean Rover tests a successful Argyll Field appraisal well whilst the world's first floating production platform, TW58, operates in the background. The Argyll Field produced the UK's first offshore oil in June 1975 and finally ceased production in October 1992 (courtesy of Malcolm Pattinson at BHP)

Petroleum Exploration Society *of Great Britain*

Tales from Early UK Oil Exploration

1960-1979

Compiled and Edited by

Richard Moreton

30th Anniversary Book

Authors and Contributors

The PESGB would like to thank the following for their contributions, without which this book would not have been possible.

General Text and Narrative

Richard Moreton

Papers / Articles

Nigel Anstey Comments on early seismic and the growth of geophysics.
Roderick I Archer 'When the Buzz word was 2-11'.
Bruce Blanche Various stories and anecdotes.
Andrew Bottomley Geoscience graduate employment statistics.
Myles Bowen 'Win some, lose some' - IMM lecture 25/10/88.
Colin Campbell Abstract from PESGB lecture 'The End of an Era - What Now?
John Church Various stories and anecdotes
Vic Colter i) 'Morecambe Gas Field', ii) 'Wytch Farm', iii) 'Lockton Gas Accumulation'.
Martin David 'History of Hydrocarbon Exploration in the Moray Firth'.
Bob Dyk and **Angus Beckett** 'The North Sea-1964', PESGB Chairman's Evening lecture 1989.
Ian Forrest i) 'The mini round of 1963', ii) 'Early Operations in the Southern Gas Province'.
Colin Fothergill 'The PESGB and North Sea Exploration - the first five years'.
Ken Glennie 'Memories of some early days of the PESGB and the release of company geological information'.
Norman Hempstead 'A history of seismic activity in the North Sea'.
Peter Hinde for permission to use material from the book 'Fortune in the North Sea' (Foulis & Co Ltd, 1966).
Jim Hornabrook 1975 paper - Seismic Interpretation of the West Sole Gas Field.
Leslie Illing 'Oil and Gas in the North Sea: the early days'.
Philip Nelson 'Bomb or Bust - Shell Expro's last dynamite line, and a well-shoot'.
Clive Randle 'The Brae (entrepreneurial) story'.
Peter Walmsley 'Reflections on the North Sea - 1965 to 1970'.
David Warwick Various anecdotes and stories.
Karen Whitehead 'Where is the PESGB in 1995?'

Other References

Adrian Hamilton 'Oil, The Price of Power' (Michael Joseph Ltd, 1986)
Woodland et al 'Petroleum and the Continental Shelf of North-West Europe' (Applied Science Publishers, 1975)

Photographs and Diagrams

Bruce Blanche, Andrew Bottomley, John Church, Ian Forrest, Colin Fothergill, Norman Hempstead, Neil McMahon, Richard Moreton, Philip Nelson, Malcolm Pattinson, Clive Randle, David Warwick.

Further Acknowledgements

Thanks go to John Brooks and his colleagues at the Department of Trade and Industry for providing advice, statistics, and a number of maps illustrating wells, fields and licensing situations at various times chronicled within these pages.

Also, thanks to British Gas, BHP, BP, Deminex, Enterprise, Texaco, University of Reading and the Westbury Hotel for providing photographs and diagrams; additional thanks to Enterprise Oil for cartographic assistance and **draft**oil for design, layout and production work.

This book was planned and organised by the **PESGB Book Committee** John Church, Ian Forrest, Colin Fothergill, Norman Hempstead, Rosemary Johnson Sabine, Richard Moreton, Paul Sandford and Peter Schwarz whose editorial input, comments, and collectively vast UK experience proved invaluable during the compilation of this volume.

Thanks go to the PESGB Office staff who have worked on this book - Karen Whitehead, the PESGB Administrative Director, and the office team of Lyn Desaleux, Johanne Powell and Rob Britton.

Finally, thanks, as always to Paul Smith for his legal advice.

......And How It All Started

The idea for a book was given to us by John Brooks of the DTI at the PESGB Christmas party of 1993. The 30th anniversaries of many aspects of UK offshore exploration were due to occur in the next year or two. John had been talking, however , to, some of the PESGB's retired members at the party. They had given him the notion that many of the stories and anecdotes about the early days would be lost as they retired from the scene.

The PESGB decided to publish a book, of 'coffee table' standard, containing as many stories, articles and pictures as we could collect to give a reflection of the professional lives of the early explorers. We also decided to make this our celebration of 30 years of PESGB activity.

We cajoled our senior members, many of whom are listed amongst the authors and contributors, to help us by excavating old material and memories. They contacted old friends and the book was born.

Special thanks should be given to Vic Colter who acted as our co-ordinator in the early stages.

Some of the stories conveyed pictures of an exciting life that those of us working in the UKCS later, regretted that we had not experienced. Some conveyed hardship. The range of recollections showed how geologists, geophysicists, and managers can have differing views of the same events. Some stories reminded us that explorers have often not received the recognition that they deserve.

Overwhelmingly, however, we were entertained and educated by what we read. We hope that you are too.

From now on perhaps you will also be inspired to file away your memories of exploration as it progresses into the 21st century so that PESGB can publish a 50th anniversary volume.

Rosemary Johnson Sabine, PESGB Chairman 1994

This book is a collection of individuals' personal recollections, which are vivid personal accounts viewed from a long distance of time, and some memories may have become blurred. It is not intended as a historical treatise, but as wonderful entertainment via exciting personal stories from individuals' viewpoints of a tremendously exciting period. The book should be read in the manner in which it was intended by individuals and the PESGB. Although the PESGB does not intend to publish any article or information containing information it knows to be inaccurate or misleading, it cannot accept responsibility for any information contained in any article or section of this book which is inaccurate or misleading and published in good faith by it. Items contained therein are contributed by individuals and do not necessarily express the opinions of the PESGB and the PESGB does not accept responsibility for the text. Reproduction of this book in any form is strictly forbidden. Usage for any commercial purpose is strictly forbidden. Any queries regarding the book should be made in writing and referred to the **Petroleum Exploration Society of Great Britain, PESGB Office, 2nd Floor, 17/18 Dover Street, London W1X 3PB**.

Petroleum Exploration Society *of Great Britain* (**PES***GB*), October 1995.

Introduction

1994 was the 30th anniversary of the foundation of the Petroleum Exploration Society of Great Britain (PESGB) and simultaneously back in 1964, highly dramatic events were beginning to unfold in the previously unexplored waters of the North Sea.

Both proved subsequently very successful, and this book celebrates and indeed remembers key events with many of the true original oil finders of that time. Read their accounts of the challenges, the euphoria and the suspense; the scrambles, the competitions and, yes, the disappointments which made these first twenty years or so of UK exploration history some of the most dramatic, memorable and rapidly evolving in the world.

This book is not one continuous account from the memory of a single nostalgic author, but a combined account - prepared from collections of short stories, tales and anecdotes culled from a variety of well known industry sources. Many of these, fully acknowledged, were written specifically for this PESGB anniversary book and truly reflect the diversity of emotions and challenges prevalent during these remarkable twenty years of exploration history, never to be repeated again in the United Kingdom - or indeed, anywhere else.

So sit comfortably, relax, and imagine the whole book is centred around a fireside dialogue with friends on a cold winter's night: everyone remembers, everyone listens, everyone contributes - and gradually the story unfolds. Those of us who weren't there can but prompt the next set of answers, and those of us who were - well, these pages are for you.

But remember, these tales are unique to our guests present - no more, no less; no bigger, no smaller. There are doubtlessly thousands of other tales to be told by all those of us out there who either smile, nod, or shake our heads while reading onwards.

But let's make that another volume.

Prologue

Please pause just a while before turning these pages
And consider in awe, irreplaceable ages
One hundred and fifty million years today
Our waters made the Kimmeridge Clay
Black shale, in quiet ocean layering
Unaware of future fortunes bearing
Hidden (anoxic) from all prying eyes
Unyielding of its rich surprise
Secretly searching for places to rest
Awaiting the courage of man's will to test
Awaiting the drill through its mile of rock travel
And surveys, permitting the truth to unravel
The seismic, the questions, the flares of first gas
The bid rounds, and build-ups to what would soon pass
The fever-pitched frenzy as enlightenment shone
And the subsurface jigsaw assembled as one
The frosty-glassed ocean through which no man could see
Shattered in pieces and the trapped oil gushed free
The boom had begun, the North Sea - come of age
In a theatre of stars with the oil centre stage
In a drama whose scenes could be harsh to endure
Through the passage of time to a future, secure
Sometimes in suspense then but often in glory
From those who delivered each tale and each story
Through labours of love, through new science and toil
Let's toast those who brought us our first North Sea oil.

RAM 95

Contents

Chapter One

How it all started - Groningen

It would probably be unfair to accuse the United Kingdom of being slow on the exploration uptake because we can, after all, only learn by experience and analogy, and in the nineteen-fifties there was little of either. Most geoscientists in the business found themselves on overseas assignments in proven petroliferous provinces where the unthinkable did not necessarily have to be thought. But that is not to say early attempts had not been made to demonstrate Britain's hydrocarbon potential, in fact, as long ago as 1936 the D'Arcy Exploration Company (now BP) had demonstrated some success - both alone and subsequently in partnership with the Gas Council in 1952 (see chapter 8). However, in the words of Peter Hinde (1966), success had not 'been striking, for the geology of this country is very small-scale, broken-up and tight. In other words the rocks generally are not continuous and porous and do not allow the early movement of fluids underground'. Which, for the seasoned explorer, perhaps made the discovery of the giant Groningen Field (just across the North Sea from the UK) even more thought-provoking.

Myles Bowen recalls his personal experience with Shell at around this time:

"After my first overseas assignment in the Far East I returned in 1958 with a small amount of savings which I thought I might invest in property. My parents, however, prevailed on me to see a cousin who was a partner in a firm of stockbrokers who, they assured me, would give me sounder advice. I remember him asking me whether oil and gas would ever be found in the North Sea; I thought of Eakring, the oil fields of West Holland and Schoonebeek and told him that I thought it most unlikely that anything of commercial significance would occur. His investment advice to me was equally bad and I lost most of my savings! A little later, in 1959, Shell discovered that I had never been involved in drilling for oil, having spent most of the previous 6 years working as a field geologist wandering around jungles and deserts with a hammer in my hand. So they sent me to Oldenzaal in the Netherlands to learn some real hydrocarbon related exploration business. While I was there sandstone cores were coming in for analysis from an exploration well which was surrounded by the utmost secrecy. I was even permitted to visit the rig, but not to know the results. The well was Slochteren-1 the discovery well of the giant Groningen gas field."

In fact the results of this well could not have been more significant. As Peter Hinde wrote in 1966:

"During the night of 14 August in the year 1959 there occurred in Holland an event whose significance has scarcely yet been grasped and whose effect on the economy of Europe will last a hundred years. It was on this night that the drilling bit at Slochteren No.1 well in northern Holland penetrated a certain sandstone which lay nearly two miles below the derrick floor. Tests carried out on this well and on subsequent wells proved beyond doubt that the reserves of natural gas contained within the pore spaces of this sandstone are huge. They are so huge that they would

be able to satisfy the present demand for gas in the United Kingdom for over 100 years.

This is a phenomenal discovery by any standard. It is so phenomenal that Slochteren No.1 well has become the most famous well since Colonel Edwin Drake drilled the world's first in Pennsylvania, in 1859. The scale of this discovery was so far in excess of anything that had gone before that the economics of petroleum exploration in Europe were changed overnight."

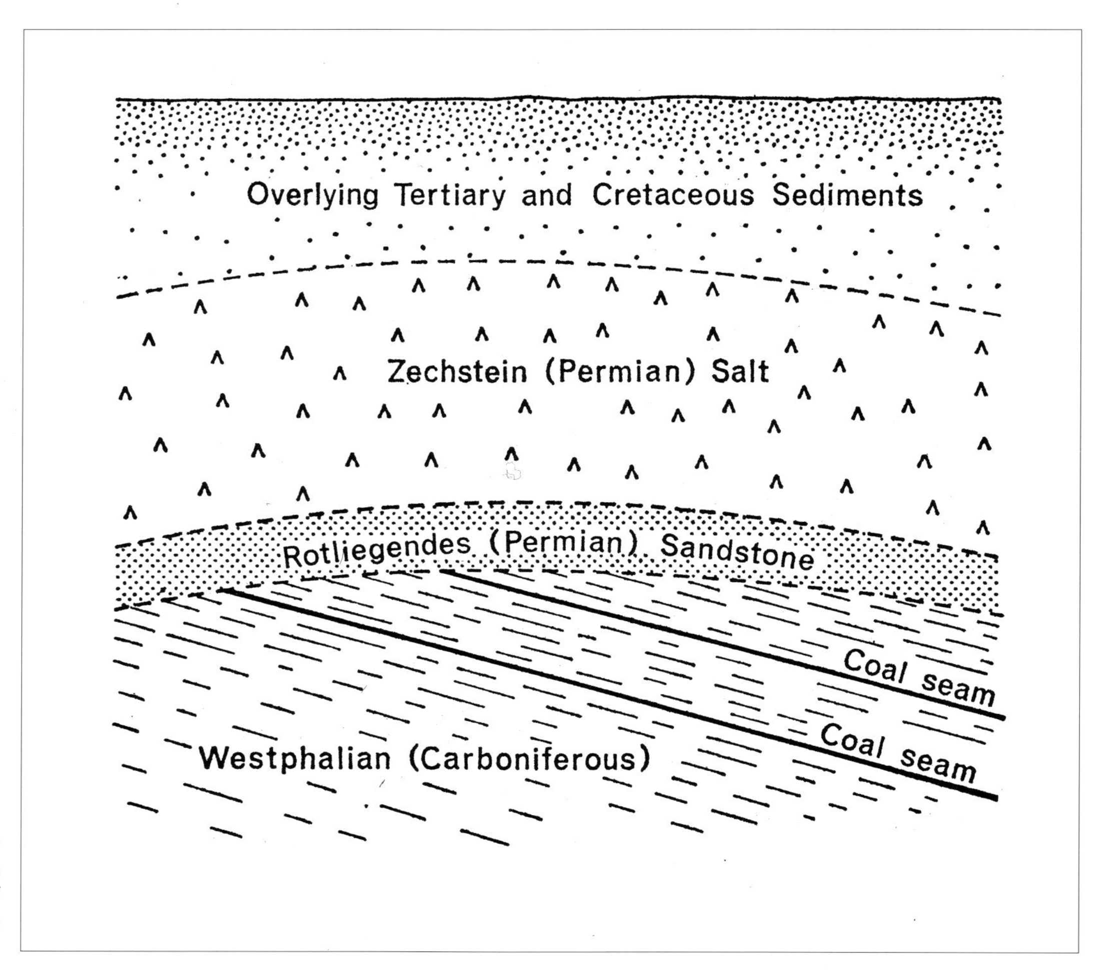

Fig 1.1
Early schematic cross-section of the Slochteren gas field.

At around 85 tcf (trillion cubic feet) this discovery was to be one of the largest in the world, and one which set all exploration geologists in geographical proximity thinking. As Leslie Illing writes:

"British geologists were quick to re-examine the correlative but thinner Lower Permian Rotliegend Yellow Sands of Durham, and speculated on prospects in the

intervening area under the North Sea. However, the offshore industry was in its infancy, and several years were to pass before the necessary marine drilling rigs, capable of operating in the decidedly hostile environment of the North Sea, were to become available."

However the race was on.

Fig 1.2
A christmas tree at Slochteren with a drilling derrick in the background.

Chapter Two

Geological Understanding at the Time

It was not unusual at the time to switch off one's brain automatically at a coastline. Myles Bowen remembers:

"At university shortly after the war, I was puzzled by the fact that geology apparently stopped at the low tide mark. Admittedly there were no data beyond that point but very few geologists attempted to extrapolate offshore. Sedimentary geology consisted largely of describing the rocks in minute detail without much regard for the wider picture. Certainly, there were a few conclusions you were permitted to draw, e.g. if you saw ripple marks on a sandstone, you were taught that it was deposited in shallow water; rubbish we now know, but in those days there were certain accepted 'truths' which no one had bothered to put to the test; the change to a more intelligent attitude to geology was to come later in the 1960s and 70s."

Just how simplified some of these earlier assumptions were is demonstrated in Fig 2.1:

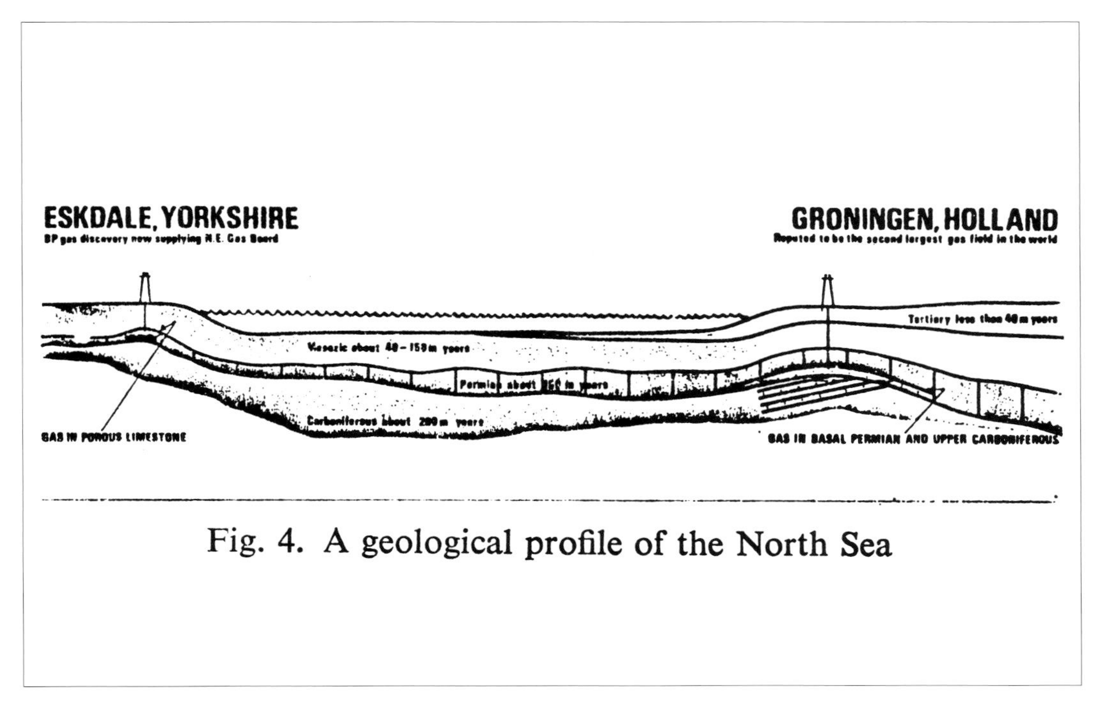

Fig. 2.1
An early geological profile of the North Sea.

But the North Sea had been considered as potentially prospective - even pre-Groningen, if only because of its surrounding neighbours. Peter Hinde wrote in 1966:

"It is true to say that there is nothing new in the idea that deposits of oil or gas may lie under the North Sea. Geologists in Britain and in other West European countries bordering the North Sea have long realised the possibilities of the existence of oil or

gas in the sedimentary deposits under the sea floor, though some oil company geologists are now claiming a retrospective enthusiasm which was not always evident at the time. With oil and gas production already achieved in England, Holland and West Germany, and with but a shallow stretch of water covering the geological joining of these lands, it was reasonable to assume that hydrocarbon deposits exist also in the North Sea area. However, on the evidence of the small oil and gas fields of Europe there was little encouragement towards the great expense of finding and developing an oilfield under the sea, the costs of which are approximately four times those of developing a similar oilfield on the land."

Of course, post Groningen, all this changed. Myles Bowen writes:

"The geology of the East Midlands area being not dissimilar to that of the northern Netherlands where the Groningen field lay, it was reasonable to imagine that the area in between might also be prospective for gas. The Permian Rotliegend sandstone primary objective reservoir was already known from Groningen while Zechstein carbonate and Bunter sandstone secondary objective reservoirs were also known from the Netherlands and Northern Germany. Jurassic and Lower Cretaceous sandstones which had hitherto been Europe's most prolific horizons for oil and gas must also have been a target. The Carboniferous and older rocks were not considered as their reservoir qualities were deemed likely to be too poor.

Source rock was also no problem as the Westphalian coals which had sourced Groningen were also present in the east Midlands and were expected to be widely distributed in the Southern North Sea. Whether they would be buried deeply enough to have produced gas may have been in doubt.

The main tricks in the search for gas were 1) seismic quality, 2) recognition of areas of inversion and 3) depth conversion. Seismic reflection went digital in the early sixties and thereafter has increased in quality continuously to the present day. Early 'plum' acreage, awarded to Shell and Esso among others, turned out to have been deeply buried and later inverted (uplifted) so that the reservoir rocks in huge and promising structures seen on seismic turned out to be essentially 'tight', the porosity and permeability of the rocks having been destroyed by diagenesis. On the other hand, had it not been for these areas of inversion, little or no gas would have been produced to charge the reservoirs."

The iterative learning process had begun.

But one area where geological knowledge was restricted was in the understanding of plate tectonics - particularly as an earlier recognition of this could have suggested possible rift basins between continental areas which could have been prolific for oil. As it stood, offshore Scotland - with its vast Pre-Cambrian and Lower Palaeozoic terrains of oily impossibility - didn't look too good! However, education was rapidly catching up. Myles Bowen says :

"One thing about British University education at that time, at least from my own experience, is that they were quite open to unconventional ideas such as Wegener's hypothesis of Continental Drift. This was seen as an attractive idea with some supporting evidence, although no one could imagine how it could actually have worked. In North America by contrast most undergraduates were taught that the idea was arrant rubbish, to be rejected without any consideration."

Bob Dyk and Angus Beckett fondly recall:

"What many of us knew about the North Sea - all geographical, nothing geological."

They continue:

"This lack of geological knowledge was in good part due to the fact that there had been little or no onshore activity to project offshore as is the case in other offshore areas. We had blindly gone into a very deep water area. Such is the courage of an explorer. Intuition and instinct are his guiding stars. It was most important to gain quickly a wide knowledge of all the surrounding countries as they were soon to follow the United Kingdom's example and offer licences. Further, any information gathered in these other areas could be vital to our work in British waters. How to get it easily and quickly was one of many problems.

Onshore well data were at a premium. Norway had no onshore prospects. There had been a number of wells drilled in Denmark but the data were not publicly available. It was suspected that there had been significant shows in the Zechstein dolomites, all non commercial. The entire offshore area was licensed to A.P. Moeller (the Danish ship owner) who, in turn had farmed out the area to some US majors. Many wells had been drilled onshore Germany and a number of fields discovered. One of the federal Geological Surveys had shot three regional seismic lines in the North Sea going as far west as the Dogger Banks. There were oil and gas fields in the Netherlands. In fact, the whole North Sea play was triggered by the discovery of the huge Groningen field in 1959.

Language and geography certainly were not the problems as far as geological information in the United Kingdom was concerned. There were excellent surface maps covering Great Britain as well as books and publications of every description. These were all available in the Geological Society of London library whose facilities were available to anyone. Significant sub-surface data was almost completely lacking, consisting of 'wells drilled in England up to 1947' as compiled by Peter Kent and Norman Falcon, somewhat out of date, but significant with respect to the Mesozoic. The simplest and most helpful book of the moment was Prof. Wills 'Palaeographic Atlas of Northwest Europe' which was purely deductive but still remarkably accurate."

Just how little was known in the early sixties is shown in Fig. 2.2, a map compiled almost entirely from gravity and magnetic surveys.

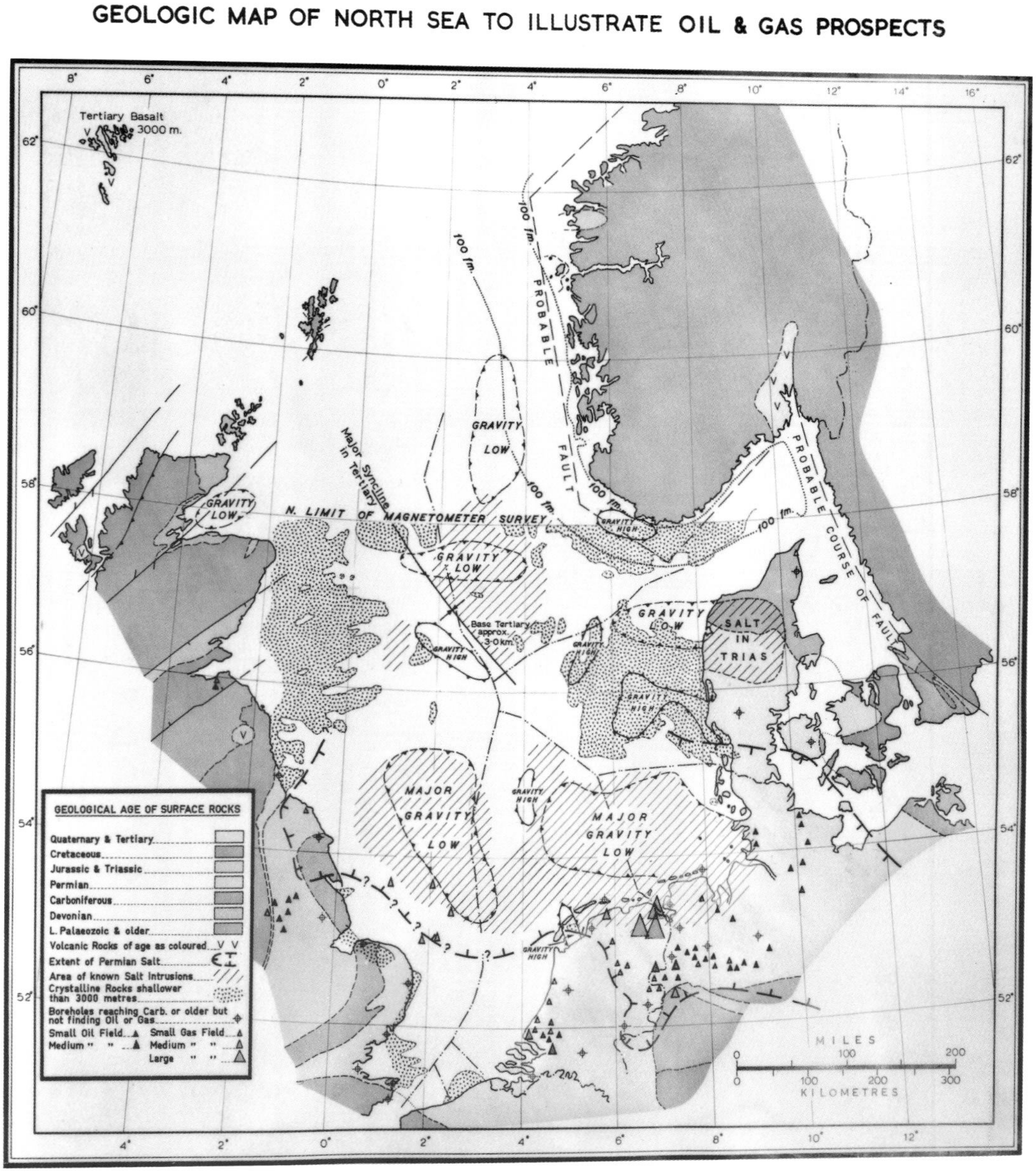

GEOLOGIC MAP OF NORTH SEA TO ILLUSTRATE OIL & GAS PROSPECTS

Fig. 2.2
Early geological map of the North Sea.

The thirst for more knowledge however was now with us and, as a part response to quench this, it was not long before the PESGB was formed to fill the gaps. Speculation continued to grow and, in anticipation of imminent licensing, seismic had already begun in 1962 and 1963.

Chapter Three

Licensing and Fiscal Background

1. **Licensing**

Myles Bowen recalls that:

"Exploitation of many of the continental shelves of the world had to await the ratification of the Geneva Convention of 1958 which had attempted to define national jurisdiction as far as the 200m isobath. Britain was the 22nd country to ratify the Convention and by doing so, in 1964, allowed it to have the force of law, so that exploration of many continental shelves worldwide could begin. This resulted in the 'carve-up' of the North Sea as we know it today.

In 1964, immediately after signing the Convention, the British government designated quadrants and blocks as far north as 61° and offered virtually the entire area, (except a corridor close to the median line) comprising 960 blocks, to the industry. The Norwegians also offered acreage in 1965, while the Dutch government did not follow suit until 1968."

The 200m isobath idea carried interesting implications and potential political disputes. Britain, for example, could have tried to claim most of Norway's continental shelf (up to the Norwegian trench of around 400m off Bergen and Stavanger!) although such a claim would almost certainly not have been upheld.

But well before the ratification of the Geneva Convention in 1964, action was already hotting up. Colin Fothergill writes:

"In 1963, oil company representatives mostly from North America flew in to meetings chaired by Alastair Matthews of BP to discuss recommendations to the Ministry of Power on the licensing terms which the companies would like to see incorporated in the regulations, based on their worldwide experience. Although this was primarily self-interest on the companies' part such a dialogue was of great benefit to the Government. Until 1964 UK governments had no experience in large scale oil exploration in a competitive commercial scenario. So these moves were welcomed by the Ministry and many of the companies' recommendations were incorporated in the legislation."

The concept of the median line was one of the key resolutions of the Geneva Convention. This is illustrated in Fig. 3.1 and was to be used when no other agreement could be reached. The median line was the locus of a point equidistant from which the nearest base line or each state from which the width of the territorial sea was to be measured. The base line was understood to be low water mark, but could be an artificial line if the coastline was irregular.

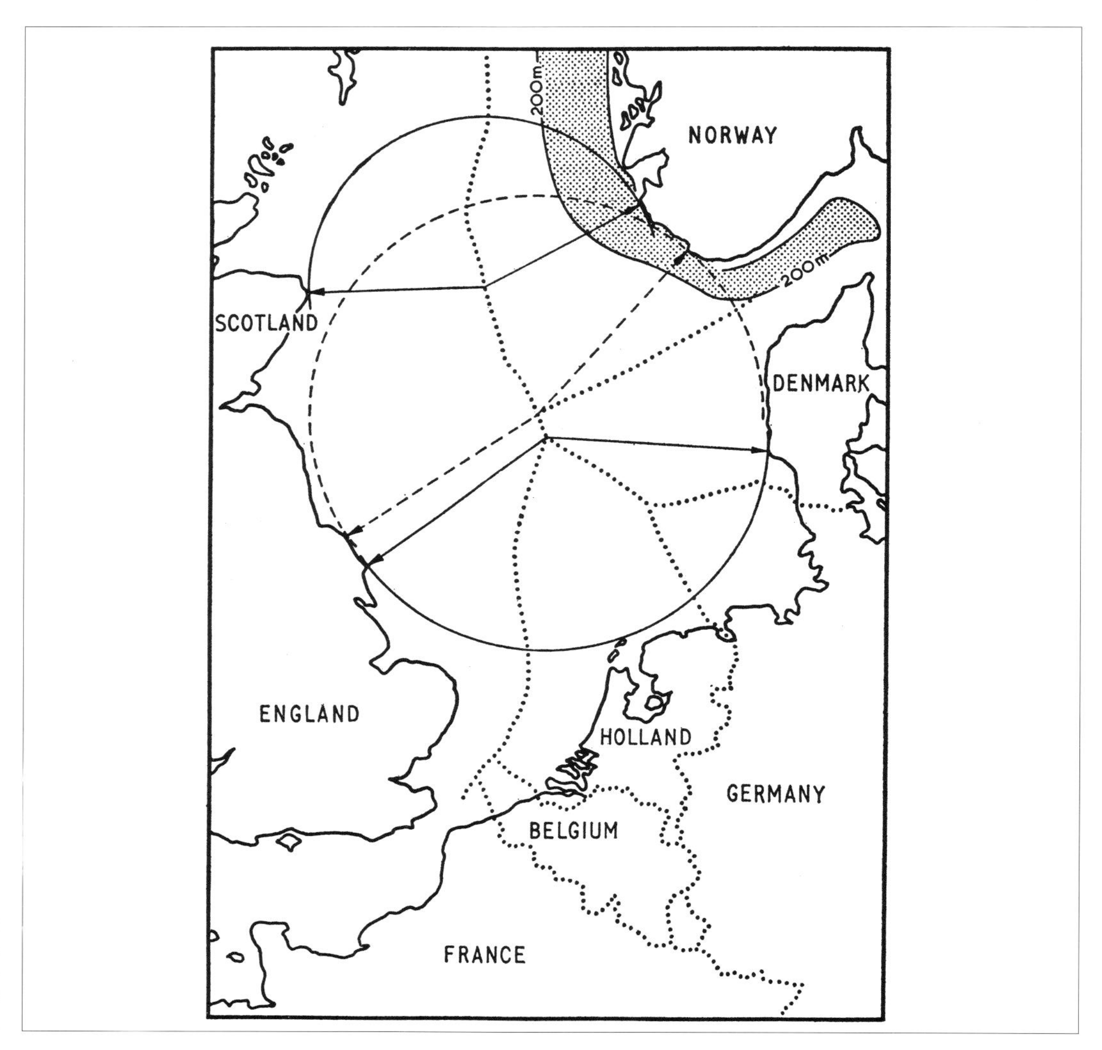

Fig 3.1
Division of the North Sea on the Median Line formula.

Ian Forrest remembers:

"Some exploration moves were initiated in 1963 under the existing onshore laws of the thirties and earlier which also covered the inshore areas out to the three-mile limit and the estuarine 'closing lines.' Some companies perhaps took the view that possession of inshore exploration concessions would improve their status in the coming (and anticipated) First Round of the Southern North Sea play.

In any case, there was a flurry of applications extending from Dorset to Norfolk and via the Wash to the Northumbrian coast. The three mile limit and the proportional rule led to severe geometric and area restrictions on the available acreage and large numbers of small permit areas had to be applied for.

Thames House was not geared up to the resulting surge of paper and maps. Urgent discussions were held with the competing operators who were invited by the Ministry to settle between themselves, by tossing coins, for first choice in areas of conflict and alternating choice thereafter.

Such a pragmatic British solution was appreciated by all parties and the resulting awards were gazetted with minimum fuss and labour.

The ensuing exploration activity included a Deep SPARKER Survey in the Kimmeridge-Purbeck coastal area and a 'conventional' shoot with explosives along the Northumbrian coast, both by the Conoco group. The latter survey provided mass inshore entertainment for the local inhabitants as well as the harvest of fish which resulted from such operations.

The reader is reminded that the average offshore shot in the area was 5lbs of dynamite detonated at frequent intervals. At Whitley Bay some 10lb charges were tried out to obtain more energy within the Carboniferous, but the pyrotechnic and blast effect along the nearby promenade put a stop to this experiment despite the enjoyment of the spectators, both on land and afloat.

A sequel to the northern survey was the Whitley Bay No.1 offshore test drilled from a coastal drill-site. The deviation technology of the sixties may have been relatively primitive but the well bottomed at planned depth and at planned offshore location.

As an amusing footnote, most of the 1963 applicants were using the same map supplier for the large orders needed in the applications. This resulted in some mis-deliveries of map orders which helped everybody concerned to keep an eye on what the competition was up to.

There was also the instance of a Texan checking out his maps in the hall of the Grosvenor House Hotel with two competitors idling nearby, just looking on.

It was a small world. The prelude to the big play."

And the prelude to a big year, because 1964 was not over yet. The passing of the Continental Shelf Act paved the way for licensing and, as Bob Dyk and Angus Beckett recall:

"In early September, as promised, the Government announced that 53 licences consisting of 394 blocks were awarded to 22 consortia involving 51 companies. Of

the 22 groups the operators of 12 were large companies, the remainder were comparative midgets.

The applicants wasted no time during the waiting period between applying for and getting licences, there were bar room sessions, lunch and dinner sessions, golf games - all in typical geological tradition dedicated to trying to find out what anybody and everybody knew about the geology of the North Sea. Needless to say, them that knew anything were not saying and the remainder had nothing to contribute."

2. **Fiscal Regime**

This is an area which has constantly evolved and changed with successive governments, economic policies, and the oil price. Indeed, one of the more heated topics of current PESGB bar-room debate concerns the recent abolition of petroleum revenue tax relief imposed by Norman Lamont in March 1993.

Martin David summarises the key points up to 1979:

"Since UK offshore exploration began in 1964, the oil price has fluctuated greatly. This has directly affected field economics which in turn has affected the levels of exploration and appraisal drilling in the North Sea.

Coupled with the variations in oil price, successive UK governments have had to develop a fiscal regime which on the one hand provides sufficient financial incentive for companies to explore and develop, while on the other hand provides suitable benefit to the economy as a whole.

The realisation in the late 60s and the early 70s of the potential of the UK as an oil producer, in 1973 led the House of Commons Public Accounts Committee to criticise the government for taking too low a 'take' compared to other oil producing countries. This situation was aggravated by the steep rise in the price of oil at this time.

After two years of discussion with the oil industry, the government passed the Oil Taxation Act of 1975, which still forms the basis of the current fiscal regime. The key provision in the act was the introduction of PRT (Petroleum Revenue Tax) based on the profits of each individual field. The initial rate was set at 45% which immediately increased the government's 'take' to 76%, compared to the previous 58% comprising royalty payments and Corporation Tax.

This clearly had an effect on levels of exploration drilling, basically dampening enthusiasm. It led to the shelving of many projects, with marginal fields becoming uneconomic. If anything, the balance swung towards developing fields which had been discovered and had received government approval for their development plans (formerly known as Annex B's).

The situation continued through the 1970s with the oil price steadily increasing. Heralded by the onset of the Iranian revolution in 1979, the oil price started to increase rapidly, and the government increased the rate of PRT to 60% in 1979, the oil price started to increase rapidly, and the government increased the rate of PRT to 60% in 1979, which increased the 'take' to 83.2%. This continued to suppress levels of exploration and appraisal drilling."

John Brooks adds:

"One of the changes which the oil taxation act brought in and which has affected PESGB members since was its requirement for fields to be 'determined' - encompassed by a boundary - and for fields to be determined on the basis of geological criteria alone."

The importance of earth sciences therefore became a **duty** (following a field discovery) rather than a pursuit applied with varying degrees of commitment by companies perhaps more eager to begin generating profits through early production.

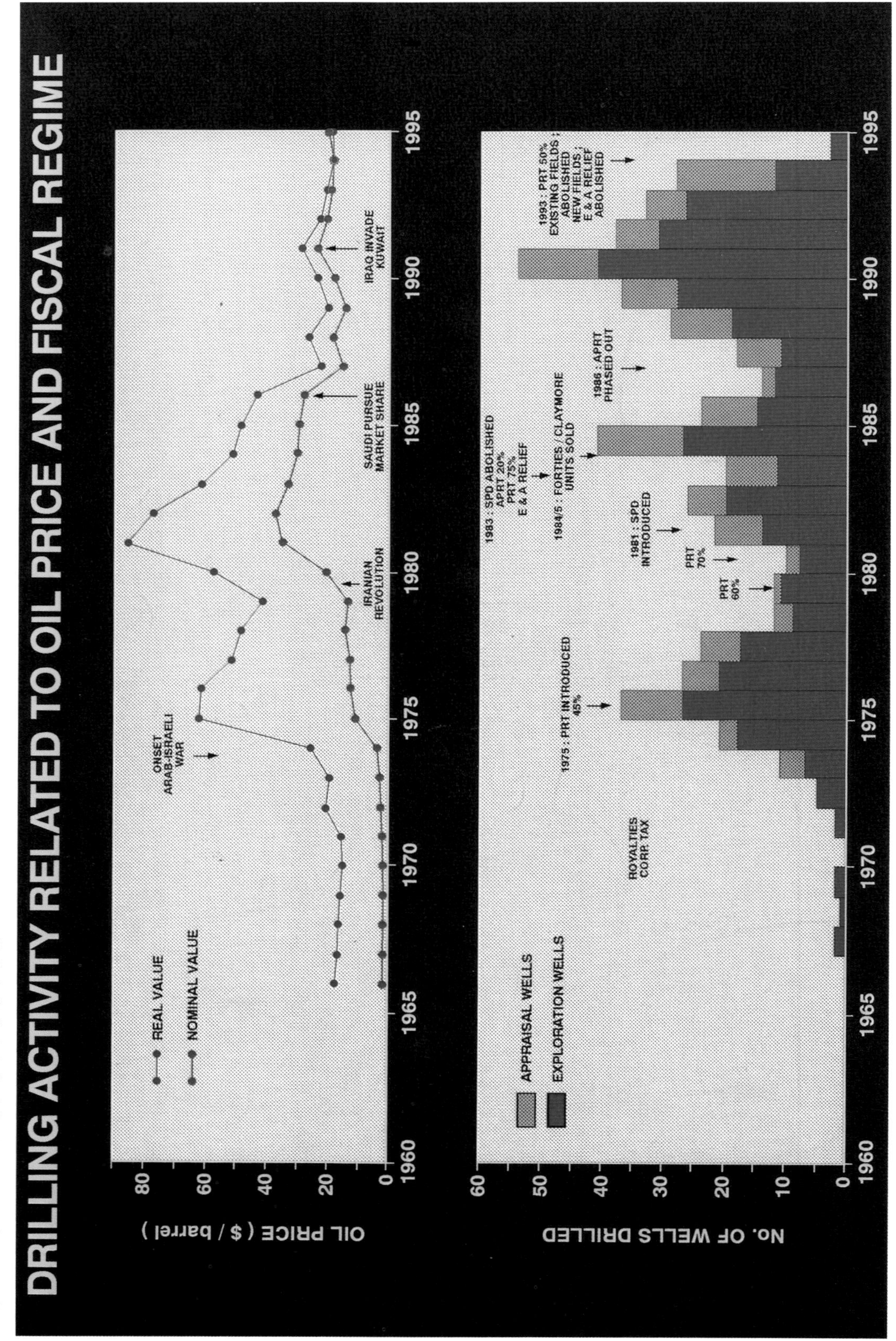

Fig. 3.2 (Top Chart) *illustrates how some economic factors operate together - particularly how oil price and fiscal regime have influenced North Sea drilling from 1966 until the present day.*

Fig. 3.3 (Bottom Chart) *illustrates drilling activity related to oil price and Fiscal regime.*

Chapter Four

Early Days : The Search for Commercial Oil

By now, with many of the major oil players of the time awaiting the results of the first Licensing Round, it is appropriate to mention some key UK names of the early sixties, and put them in the context of future developments. Colin Fothergill provides the following account:

"One of two individuals who had an immense influence on the course of exploration from that time was Angus Beckett. As Undersecretary in the Petroleum Division of the Ministry of Power he was largely responsible for the legislation of 1964, the blocks offered in the licensing rounds and the allocation of awards of licence blocks. From a total of 960 blocks offered on 15th May 1964 there were 31 applications (involving 61 separate corporate bodies and individuals) for 394 blocks, and on 17th September the Minister of Power announced the award of 53 licences which included 51 companies. Most of the world's major companies were represented and many others. The 'favoured' belt for applications and awards was the southern North Sea where there were about eight applications for every block. British participation was about 30% and included the small British independent Trinidad Canadian Oils (later renamed Tricentrol). The remainder was largely US based companies but Canadian participation was about 10%. All had substantial work programmes imposed.

It is sometimes forgotten that quite a few of the pioneers of oil exploration in the early days in the North Sea were independents from North America who had only limited experience overseas but who had years of offshore experience in their own 'backyards'. Companies who operated offshore in the Gulf Coast or off California, for example, provided invaluable expertise in the untested environment of the UK Continental Shelf. The know-how brought to the UK by North American oilmen enabled exploration and drilling to get off to a flying start in 1964 after the first licences were awarded, and ensured the high level of activity which followed. This scenario, unique at the time, reminds us too of the daunting environmental and engineering challenges which presented themselves when drilling started in the North Sea during those first five years.

The remarkable speed in which the First Round was handled also ensured that appraisal of prospects proceeded rapidly and was a tribute to the skill and efficiency of Angus Beckett who, almost single handed, decided the recommendations to the Minister on the allocation of licences. Angus was a forthright individual and early in his career had been a schoolmaster and a request to be interviewed by him to discuss work programmes was rather like being summoned to the headmaster's study. I remember on one occasion waiting for a meeting with him during a later round of licensing sitting next to Paul Getty and his aides on the old sofa in the corridor outside his room in Thames House on Millbank. Getty seemed equally apprehensive as myself about the forthcoming interrogation! Angus became a highly respected figure in the oil community and a great friend of the PESGB as well.

He addressed the Society on more than one occasion and was later made an Honorary Member.

All companies applying for licences have to be registered in the UK, and for small companies these were mostly looked after by law firms in London, but when the licences were issued there was an influx of geologists and geophysicists from North America who set up offices in London to represent their companies. At the same time drilling and geophysical contractors and other service companies built up their staffs, and domestic job opportunities for British geologists and geophysicists began to expand.

Until the North Sea opened up there were in fact relatively few career opportunities for geologists and geophysicists with UK oil companies. Mining geology offered better job opportunities in those days and there were only a handful of British companies involved in oil exploration. Most graduates joined Shell, BP, Burmah or one of the smaller companies like Trinidad Leaseholds or Attock Oil, and faced an overseas career for most of their working life.

The second major figure in those early days was Bob Dyk. He had formerly worked as a geophysicist in Libya and when interest in the North Sea developed he was based in Brussels and consulted for Hamilton Brothers. He first made his mark in the UK in the consultation procedures with the Ministry of Power before the First Round and after the awards he was quick to recognise the need for a society of oil explorationists in Britain. Together with Howard Karren of Monsanto and the support of others he formed the PESGB with ideas based on his experience with the Petroleum Exploration Society of Libya. Informal invitations were sent to his friends and colleagues to a first meeting at The Westbury Hotel in December 1964.

Some forty of us were present and this was the start of a camaraderie amongst North Sea oil explorationists which has continued over the years. Many of the founder members or those who joined soon after worked with oil companies in London but there were also representatives from universities, government and the service companies. Several were notable in different fields and sadly are no longer with us: Angus Beckett, Professor Dan Gill of the Royal School of Mines, Ian MacCartney of Amoco, Donald Brown ex Shell, and Peter Kent of BP (later knighted for his services to oil exploration).

Bob Dyk who became Chairman in 1965 had a long record of distinguished service not only to the PESGB but also to the North Sea oil industry as a whole. He became an Honorary Member of the Society and was active in many organisations including the North Sea Operators' Committee. For his services to the industry he was awarded (as a US citizen) an honorary CBE. He could not have envisaged in December 1964 that 30 years on our membership would have reached 4,000. When he died in 1991 he had become a father figure in the UK offshore oil industry and the success of the PESGB over the years is a tribute to his enthusiasm and dedication to the importance of its role in UK oil exploration.

As in subsequent rounds the work commitments in the First Round involved seismic followed by drilling. If seismic results did not justify drilling then licensees were expected to negotiate a relinquishment of the licence. This 'drill or drop' philosophy was followed in subsequent rounds and companies were not held to a drilling obligation unless a drillable prospect was defined. Some companies had already delineated prospects by late 1964 and Amoseas (Standard Oil Company of California and Texaco) spudded the first well in block 38/29 on 26th December 1964. This was a dry hole, as were several others drilled the following year in quadrants later recognised to be on the Mid-North Sea High. It was not until several years later that the structural pattern of the North Sea became known in any detail and the barren nature of this part of the shelf was appreciated."

Texaco UK, in their January 1995 issue of news magazine 'Agenda' quote sixties Drilling Supervisor Dick de Mestre on the legendary rig Mr Cap (see Fig. 4.1) which drilled this first North Sea well - probably (due to the harsh climate) not originally intended to be there!:

"It had worked before off Zeeland in 70' of water - hardly offshore"

Of subsequent operations, he comments:

"As far as we were concerned, it was a job. It was a job and it was rougher than anywhere else. The main thing was not to lose your rig. The seas could be huge. The waves were over 100' high sometimes. Why we didn't go up in the air I don't know."

Colin Fothergill continues:

"Drilling and seismic activity through 1965 was mainly in the southern North Sea and efforts were concentrated on seeking prospects in the 'prime target'; namely the basal Permian Rotliegend sand, productive in the Slochteren gas field. It was already established that gas trapped in the sand had been generated from deeply buried coal measures and was sealed by overlying Permian Zechstein salt. Secondary targets in this region were onlap prospects where Mesozoic formations wedge out southwards on to the London Brabant Platform.

It was however the delineation of structures at the base of the Permian which mostly taxed the minds of geologists and geophysicists at the time. The single fold analogue seismic did enable some reflections to be carried over considerable distances, but it was difficult to determine details of structure below the high velocity salt; this was critical to locating Rotliegend prospects in what was to become known as the Southern Gas Basin. Refined interpretation was not possible because multiple reflections and reverberation problems obscured stratigraphical detail, and it was not until about the mid to late 1960s that seismic techniques had advanced sufficiently (with digital recording and processing and multiple coverage) to map in depth closed features on top of the Rotliegend. As sonic logs became available velocity control improved but a number of wells were drilled in the early years on spurious highs due to velocity 'pull up' in structures containing thick salt of high velocity."

Fig. 4.1
'Mr Cap' drilling the first well in the North Sea.

There are many accounts of exploration life in the early sixties - particularly from Britons who were returning to their homeland from various exploration locations to begin work in their own backyards. Peter Walmsley provides us with these early reflections of life with BP (when pecuniary attractions were clearly not a geologist's main incentive!):

"In October 1965 I was posted from Trinidad to Eakring in Nottinghamshire to become BP's first North Sea review geologist. At the age of 36, with 14 years of experience behind me, I was quite gratified to be offered a salary of £2,100 per annum.

It was not the most demanding of jobs. BP had data from 3 wells; 44/11-1 drilled jointly with Hamilton Brothers, plus exchange data from Amoseas 38/29-1 and Shell 44/2-1. I had no access to seismic data or maps, nor to the information from the currently drilling 48/6-1 (the West Sole discovery well) despite meeting the rig geologists daily. Such information was far too confidential to be entrusted to the review geologist!

BP's North Sea operations were then conducted out of Cleethorpes from Eakring. The two rig geologists and I reported to Frank Howitt who, as senior geologist, also looked after onshore activities. He in turn was technically responsible to Geoff Brunstrom, the regional geologist for Europe in London. Geoff worked closely with John Wood, the regional geophysicist, who had a small team working on North Sea geophysics in a secure office in Basinghall Street, just off London Wall. This group was headed by Doc Wyrobek.

At Eakring the security of data was considered far more important than providing the budget to ensure its safety. No office furniture had locks. BP still owes me for the hasp and padlock which I bought from Woolworths and fitted to my cupboard as a precaution against my 3 sets of well logs going walk-about. Frank, who had in his possession a few geophysical maps and the 48/6-1 well logs, resorted to hiding them amongst the thousands of East Midlands coal seam maps which BP had over the years acquired from the National Coal Board.

Fig. 4.2
'Sea Gem' flaring off gas from the North Sea's first commercial discovery - before tragedy struck.

Whilst this represented the ultimate in security it presented certain data retrieval problems and it could well be that some of this material may still lie there undiscovered to this day! By the beginning of December 1965 excitement was mounting at Eakring as it became known that the testing of 48/6-1 had proved the presence of North Sea gas in commercial quantities for the very first time. We therefore broke up for Christmas in cheerful mood. How sadly that mood was to change. I can remember so vividly listening to the evening news at home in Surrey the day after Boxing Day to hear the announcement that the Sea Gem had capsized with the loss of 13 lives whilst jacking down to move location. It was in sombre mood that we returned to Eakring after the holiday."

In fact the collapse of the 'Sea Gem' was a double disaster; first and clearly foremost for the men killed and their kin, but also because it provided such an unfitting end to the first well to discover Groningen analogues close to Britain. It also occurred on the first year anniversary of the commencement of drilling in the British North Sea (Amoseas - Mr Cap), another ironic twist in the tale. Peter Hinde describes the tragic incident:

"It was at 2.30pm that the Sea Gem was said to be jacking up a notch prior to jacking down to sea level - the usual procedure. The well had been completed and the platform was to have moved out to drill another well some two miles to the west, to help prove the field. Suddenly the platform lurched, dropped at one corner and slowly plunged beneath the waves to finish upside down on the bottom. Two of the 10 legs became detached from the platform and finished up 250ft south and 200ft east of the wreckage. Thirteen men were killed."

In memory of this tragic incident, many of the 19 survivors attended a recent reunion dinner on the 6th July 1995. They are pictured below.

But, whatever the cost of some of these early operations - both in human terms and

Fig. 4.3 Reunion dinner hosted by BP Exploration XEU in 1995 for the Survivors of the Sea Gem tragedy.

in various attributable down time costs, it is important to appreciate that we were not really dealing with new technologies here (in a worldwide sense) - simply the harsh reality of operating, within the public eye, close to home.

Ian Forrest provides an account of some of these early operations in the Southern Gas province:

"The selection of drilling platforms covered the spectrum from floating ship-shape drill ships through jack-ups to fixed-leg structures. The drill ship results were not encouraging due to the seasonal agitation of the shallow sea. This led to instability, loss of anchors and wet-ship conditions giving rise to interruptions in drilling progress and even loss of hole.

It is surprising that few statistics seem to have been collected up to that time about, for example, wave height and frequency in this shallow-water area. I clearly remember being ridiculed by a well-known boating correspondent who, despite his experience, refused to believe that 30 foot waves were measured in storm periods in the southern areas off Yarmouth.

This marine agitation had to be suffered in silence by employees of those companies which did not use helicopters for staff movements to the rigs, relying only on fast crew boats or work boats. This required the last (or first) leg of the trip being via the crane-hoisted basket. This part could be a daunting experience in the best of conditions for some people without a head for heights but it was a veritable roughhouse in bad weather. I remember, for example, the Schlumberger operator being dumped waist- deep in the sea while clinging to the outside of the basket and then next partially disappearing down the ship's funnel as the crane-man desperately did his best to correct for the ship's violent movements in a high sea.

The safety of the Schlumberger operator was naturally much more important when he was leaving the platform than when arriving since the original records of the survey were with him in the basket on his way back to shore. The client company had its priorities clear. However, the 100' high basket trip did lend some piquancy to life, although the accident/injury figures for this method of vertical locomotion are not known. Passengers were forbidden to enter the basket on safety grounds since there would be more danger inside than outside in the event of a spill into the sea. The interior of the basket was obviously reserved for baggage, (see Fig. 4.4).

The sea trip in a work boat in rough weather was also an experience for landlubbers to remember, although the so-called fast crew boats took the biscuit in bad conditions with one record trip time of 17 hours for the 55 miles of rough water from the rig to Yarmouth.

A fixed-leg platform was used by Conoco in its first series of exploration wells. Constructed in Holland from Stateside models, it was a company-owned multi-

Fig. 4.4
All aboard for lift-off on a calm day.

legged table-top which was handled off and on to a barge for each well. The drilling equipment and accommodation had to be lifted off and on individually so there were considerable rigging up and down periods making weather a significant factor. On one occasion the empty accommodation unit was dropped and lost.

It speaks much for Conoco's confidence that its early exploration wells in the Southern North Sea were drilled from production platforms (see Fig. 4.5).

Fig. 4.5
Conoco's first exploration well 49/17-1 drilled from a production - type platform Conoco -1.

The cost-saving of this platform kept drilling budgets to about $150,000 (old money) for a 10,000' exploration well. We should not forget that dry hole costs were subsidised to the tune of about 30% by a very sympathetic Minister of Energy called Tony Benn who obviously felt that capitalist investment had to be encouraged especially after the adversity of an unsuccessful well. He did not want us to lose heart and it was only taxpayers' money anyway.

Conoco drilled several wells before bringing the National Coal Board in as earning partner into its fully-owned acreage. The first Conoco well was 49/17-1 which proved 36' of gross sandstone pay in the Rotliegend. This result was not sufficiently interesting to follow up locally but, given the quality of the seismic detail on smaller structures at that time it was a reasonable first try.

There was however a hidden explanation for the disappointing result since the first-choice location for 49/17-1 was in a water depth which was too shallow for use of the fixed-leg platform. The shift to the required depth of water was all down-dip, so the original location could probably have given an exploitable result affecting the future sequence of events for Conoco. Subsequently the major Viking Field was discovered in a separate structural block nearby, this time using a jack-up rig.

The National Coal Board was a major beneficiary in this field. In these pre-Scargill days when there were hundreds of gas-works all over the country I remember discussing in NCB's Northumberland H.Q. in early 1963 with Mike Clark the pros and cons of coal, oil and gas as national resources. Mike was then an NCB geophysicist who had pioneered offshore seismic/sparker for the Coal Board with some success in the sub-sea Carboniferous and Permian sands section where mine workings extended up to five miles offshore. The NCB was concerned at the time with the loss of its coal gas and other coal markets to offshore methane in the wake of the Dutch discoveries and the Algerian imports. It was accustomed to writing-off losses in the mega scale but it did not need much tuition in assessing the comparative risks of gas exploration by offshore drilling compared to the slow and costly development and recoupment from new coal mines. Mike knew that 'if you can't beat them, join them' and with Lord Robens at the helm, the national coal company eventually took the big step of getting into the domain of its oil company competitors. There was a logic in joining with Conoco which was already a major coal producer in U.S.A.

The British National Oil Corporation later took over the offshore assets of the National Coal Board. This was less a change in the ownership of a part of the national energy reserve than a change in its bookkeepers.

The association of evaporites and hydrocarbon entrapment has been well documented in many oil patches throughout the world and the North Sea areas include many examples of both the effective sealing medium of salt above the

Rotliegend and Carboniferous gasometers (and their Coal Measures gas works) and the favourable structural deformation of the younger beds by mobilised salt.

It may be out of place to make mention here of a salt-related fairy tale (not by Hans Andersen) from Denmark's distant pre-war exploration history but it is essentially part of the folk-lore of the North Sea Basin.

The pre-war well Harte-1 was drilled by an American entrepreneur who later transferred his countrywide Danish concession to Gulf Oil. The intensive post-war programme of Gulf followed the Zechstein oil play in South Denmark and chased Cretaceous and Jurassic sand prospects further north in what turned out to be a significant evaporite basin with mobilised salt in the northern areas. There were no discoveries, since the Mesozoic section was immature while the Zechstein contained no economically useful reservoirs (to date) and was not linked to good source material. Major salt reserves were of course established but the market for that product is limited.

The Harte-1 well had logged and warehoused a cored salt section from in or beneath the Cretaceous. This evidence would have helped high grade Denmark to any keen wildcatter with Stateside experience, and since there was already some oil production from Zechstein carbonates in North Germany.

However it transpired that the Harte-1 salt cores were full diameter and had been cut and removed while drilling with fresh-water mud - a fairy tale indeed - nay a miracle. There was only one conclusion possible, the cores had been obtained elsewhere - probably from Germany. The well had been truly salted in the cause of progress.

The ingenuous ingenuity of the perpetrator of the evaporitic non-event did of course act as a catalyst to exploration in Denmark but that country, with hindsight, did not need any such miraculous happening in praise of the Zechstein.

As a green geologist in 1950-53 in Denmark with Gulf, I remember the finality of a well when it encountered the red beds beneath the Zechstein when the toolpusher developed thoughts for rigging down and the move to the next location. These were the so called 'suitcase sands' with the unmistakable portent of a dry hole. Perhaps the same biblical truth was accepted in Holland up to the huge 'accidental' gas discovery by NAM in these contemptible red beds."

But back to the UK, where oil companies had already firmly established themselves. Most chose to locate in London (Aberdeen had not yet taken off) but there were some exceptions. Colin Fothergill continues with his early North Sea story:

"One exception was Burmah Oil whose North Sea subsidiary, Burmah Oil Exploration, under Bryce Cameron acquired a hotel in Scarborough as an office to

handle North Sea operations. Burmah took a major role in the oil community for many years and it was Bryce Cameron's idea, together with David Goodwill of Amoseas, to form a North Sea Operators' Committee. One remembers Burmah's generous hospitality in the congenial surroundings on the sea front at Scarborough.

Enthusiasm engendered by the First Round encouraged the Ministry to hold a Second Round in 1965 and over 1000 blocks were offered. Coming so soon after the First Round it attracted only 21 applications for 127 blocks and only 37 licences were awarded. Companies were still exploring First Round licences and were constrained by seismic and drilling commitments. But as in the First Round there was strong interest by non oil companies - ICI, for example was a member of the Burmah North Sea group which was awarded 26 blocks. In the Second Round several new companies came in, including Allied Chemical, and this trend of non oil company interest in getting on to the band wagon continued in later rounds; particularly in the Fourth Round in 1971/72 after commercial oil had been found. Another development in the Second Round was the offering of offshore blocks outside the North Sea - notably the English Channel. The presence of oil seeps along the Dorset coast and the discovery of the small oilfield in Kimmeridge Bay had for long aroused interest in the onshore and offshore prospects of the Dorset - Hampshire coastal belt, and a range of blocks were put on offer following discussions with industry and academics.

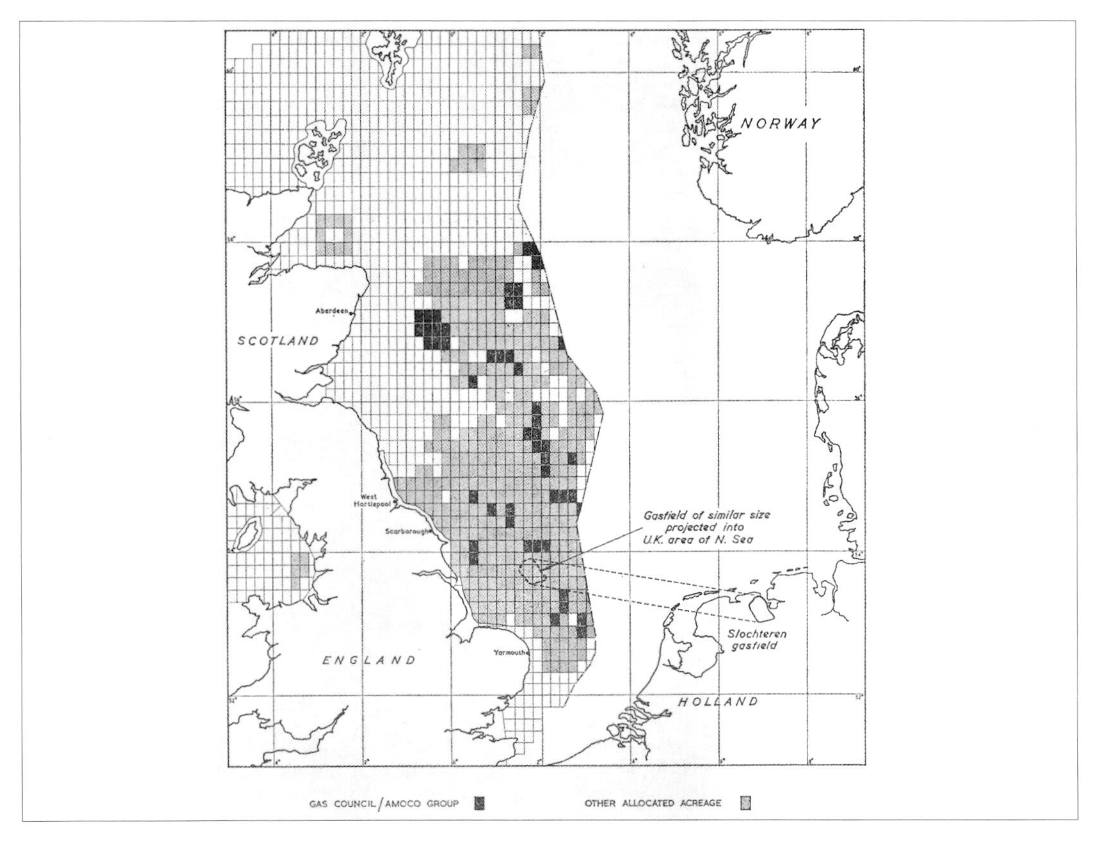

Fig. 4.6
Allocation of the North Sea acreage after two rounds of applications.

Exploration in the Southern North Sea continued to be given priority through 1966 and the discovery of the West Sole field at the end of 1965 accelerated drilling activity still further.

1966 also saw further important gas discoveries in blocks awarded in the First Round; Leman Bank (Shell) in April in 49/26-1; Indefatigable (Amoco) in June in 49/18-1; and Hewett (Arco) in October in 48/29-1. There were a few minor oil discoveries, as in Burmah's 48/22-1 well in Zechstein carbonates, but early hopes of finding oil in significant amounts did not materialise at that time. During 1966 exploration also moved north into the deeps of the Tertiary basin where a few Tertiary structures were tested without success. It was still to be several years before the basins and grabens in the north were to be actively explored and exploration was still concentrated in the 'favoured belt'. The discovery of Hewett in block 48/29 however opened up a new target when gas was discovered in Trias sands in an anticlinal fault block. Here Rotliegend gas had migrated up faults bounding the structure on the northeast side and it was hoped that other similar structures elsewhere in the favoured belt would be gas bearing."

Peter Walmsley also well recalls 1966 well - the first year he returned to London from Eakring:

"In March 1966 I was posted back to London to undertake my review geology within Doc Wyrobek's geophysical group in Basinghall Street. At last BP was beginning to appreciate the benefits of integrating the work of geophysicists and geologists! It was an exciting year. BP had taken delivery of Sea Quest, UK's first semi-submersible, from Harland and Wolf in Belfast.

By mid-year it had embarked on the delayed appraisal of West Sole, the rig sitting on the sea bed, rather than floating, because of the water depth. Twenty seven wells were drilled in the North Sea that year, compared with nine in the previous year. Rigs were hard to come by. Conoco built a fixed platform to drill 48/12-1 and it was subsequently dismantled and moved to drill two further wells. Discoveries followed fast; Leman in April, Indefatigable in June and Hewett in October. The North Sea was booming.

It was at about this time that BP's Chief Geologist, Norman Falcon, retired and his successor, Peter Kent, took over as Exploration Manager. Norman had played a major role in pushing for North Sea exploration and advising on the regime under which it could be undertaken. He must feel more than satisfied at the subsequent success spawned by his early efforts.

BP was now accumulating much more well data by exchange and I was now in a position to utilise the rapidly increasing pool of seismic sections and maps. No longer was the job undemanding; indeed, it was the very reverse!"

Fig. 4.7
The first producing platform in the North Sea - BP's fixed leg production platform 'A' in the West Sole Gas Field.

And activity continued to grow. Table 4.8 shows the first thirteen wells drilled in the UK North Sea, between December 1964 and April 1966.

TABLE 7:1—A BAKER'S DOZEN
THE WELLS DRILLED IN THE U.K. NORTH SEA
IN ORDER OF SPUDDING IN

	Group	*Well No.*	*Spudded*	*Vessel*	*Contractor*	*Location*	*Water Depth ft.*	*Remarks*
1.	Amoseas	38-29-1	26.12.64	Mr. Cap	Global Marine	55° 3·2′ N 2° 39·8′ E	85	No commercial hydrocarbons. Abandoned.
2.	Shell	44-2-1	5.4.65	Mr. Cap	Global Marine	54° 52′ 40″ N 2° 23′ 27″ E	80	Dry. Completed 21.6.65 Abandoned.
3.	Gulf	53-10-1	24.4.65	Glomar IV	Global Marine	52° 44′ 0″ N 2° 51′ 0″ E	115	Dry. Abandoned.
4.	B.P.	48-6-1	5.6.65	Sea Gem	B.P.	53° 42′ 30″ N 1° 08′ 22″ E	85	Commercial gas in Rotliegendes. Non-commercial gas in Zechstein.
5.	Total	44-21-1	5.7.65	Neptune	Soc. de Forages en Mer 'Neptune'	54° 10′ 54″ N 2° 08′ 10″ E		Dry. Abandoned.
6.	Gulf	49-13-1	7.65	Glomar IV	Global Marine	53° 32′ 15″ N 2° 32′ 30″ E		Junked
7.	Continental	49-17-1	28.8.65	Conoco I	Loffland Bros.	53° 26′ 28″ N 2° 19′ 26″ E	90	3·6 MMSCFD in Rotliegendes plus water. Well abandoned.
8.	Signal	41-20-1	9.9.65	Endeavour	Global Marine	54° 21′ 40″ N 0° 05′ 20″ W	180	11 miles off Scarborough. Dry. Abandoned.
9.	Shell	49-19-1	29.9.65	Neptune	Soc. de Forages en Mer 'Neptune'	53° 20′ 48″ N 2° 45′ 26″ E		Dry. Abandoned.
10.	Phillips	49-6-1	15.10.65	North Star	International Drilling	53° 42′ 19″ N 2° 05′ 03″ E		Possible commercial gas.
11.	Shell	49-26-1	10.12.65	Neptune	Soc. de Forages en Mer 'Neptune'	53° 05′ 12″ N 2° 07′ 42″ E		Commercial gas in the Rotliegendes.
12.	Burmah	42-23-1	27.1.66	Ocean Prince	Odeco (U.K.) Ltd.	54° 15′ 51″ N 0° 34′ 43″ E	210	
13.	Gas Council	49-18-1	8.4.66	Mr. Louie	Reading & Bates	53° 23′ 36″ N 2° 31′ 26″ E	112	Gas in the Rotliegendes.

Table 4.8
'A Baker's dozen'.

Moving on now to 1967, Colin Fothergill remembers:

"One of the most active companies in North Sea drilling in those early years was again Burmah who drilled a number of wells in the gas basin using the ill-fated Ocean Prince semi-submersible platform which was later to break up in heavy seas.

Fig. 4.9
The 'Ocean Prince' semi-submersible.

As hopes for another Hewett receded, Burmah and others were drilling structures close to the Norfolk coast and near the Wash in the Mesozoic onlap belt where it was thought that Rotliegend gas (and possibly oil) might have migrated updip into pinch-out traps. Burmah, Placid, Phillips and Arpet were probably the most active in drilling to test this concept but results were disappointing and most of the blocks have long since been relinquished. It is arguable whether prospects in onlap traps have yet been fully evaluated and the quality of seismic available at that time also militated against effective definition of stratigraphic traps in low relief structures. Placid apparently found significant amounts of gas and some oil in 48/21-1 in the Rotliegend and named the discovery Gudgeon, but this did not become commercial. On the other hand Signal in 53/4-1 discovered gas in Zechstein carbonates southeast of Leman Bank and further drilling established the small Scram accumulation."

John Church adds:

"Mention of 53/4-1 reminds me of my first offshore experience which highlighted the fact that although the American companies were by far and away the most experienced in offshore exploration they still needed, occasionally, some home grown assistance.

I had joined Robertson Research in 1964 and initially had worked on Middle East wells but quickly became involved in the North Sea when Gulf drilled, what was, the third well in the offshore UK- 49/13-1. Eventually in 1967 I got my chance to go and join the 'real men' at the sharp end when Dick Bannister of Signal Oil and Gas requested the services of a wellsite stratigrapher on the 53/4-1 well to identify a thin Lower Cretaceous sand objective sitting on the Triassic. Even with my limited experience I thought this was optimistic, even supposing one could restrain the drillers. However, I was really keen to 'do my bit' and turned up at Great Yarmouth, donned a survival suit and staggered with my equipment to the chopper. I vividly remember that the helicopter was mounted on floats, which I neatly crushed as I staggered (under the weight of my microscope and other miscellaneous gear I hasten to add) to get aboard unaided by the phlegmatic bunch of passengers already ensconsėd in their seats.

Once on the rig (the Zapata Endeavour) I quickly got down to work and found that I was the fifth geologist on board. As well as the Signal geologist, Marathon had sent one, and both the Baroid personnel were also geologists. As I had anticipated the drillers zoomed out of the Chalk, through the thin Lower Cretaceous before I had had any chance to see my sand (let alone date it) and into red beds. At this point my job was done, or so I thought, and I suggested that Signal could dispense with my services - this was not to be!

Whether Dick Bannister, the Exploration Manager of Signal, thought it would be good for my soul or not I was kept on. Initially not one of the geologists, including myself knew where we were in the section - were the red shales Triassic or Permian? I thought I should defer to the superior experience of the wellsite geologists but soon realised that this was a figment of my imagination. I became aware, thanks to coaching from Cyril Haskins, that I was the only one on board who knew about the Rögenstein Ooliths, which occur in the Lower Bunter and which I was starting to pick up in the samples (Robertson Research from the beginning had always emphasised that it was imperative to understand the lithostratigraphy as well as the fossils). I was then able to suggest that the Zechstein dolomites would soon be encountered and, more or less on schedule, buff dolomites appeared. I duly suggested that these were from the Zechstein, since again nobody else seemed to be able to identify them other than as dolomite. At the same time gas was recorded and the Wissey accumulation had been discovered. 'Right' I thought, 'I can really be of assistance now with the lithostratigraphy' but others thought differently because the message came - 'send the bugman ashore!' "

While a number of wells at the time found only small accumulations or required more appraisal drilling, there were plenty of 'near misses'. Myles Bowen recalls:

"Of the early wells, perhaps the most successful on the UK side was drilled in 1967 by Gulf jointly with Shell. It was 22/11-1 which found and tested oil from thin Palaeocene sands, but was deemed non-commercial. The test was carried out over a 490 ft interval and recovered only 60 barrels of oil and gas cut mud.

Fortunately for me it was not, as we at Enterprise would not have had the opportunity of discovering (or re-discovering) the Nelson field in the same area 20 years later. But that is another story!"

We are now getting close to one of the North Sea's key years; commercial oil was discovered in 1969. By contrast, 1968 was a relative anticlimax considering the discoveries of 1967 and did little to boost confidence for that elusive goal. Colin Fothergill says:

"1968 saw further discoveries but not as significant as in the previous year. One of these, Rough, was found by Gulf in 47/8-1 and was considered only just commercial. Situated fairly close to the Lincolnshire coast it later became well known when it was taken over by British Gas to become the world's first storage reservoir offshore. There was some disappointment that no further gas fields on the scale of Leman Bank or Indefatigable had been found and prospects for commercial oil in the Southern Gas Basin seemed slim."

Chapter Five

Early Seismic and the Growth of Geophysics

With the relative unknowns in the North Sea after the Groningen discovery seismic data were a must. From the early analogue lines to the first digital data recorded in 1964, the geophysicist became an essential team player in the search for hydrocarbons.

Nigel Anstey sets the scene:

'Bliss was it in that dawn to be alive,
But to be young was very heaven.'
(Wordsworth)

"How to convey the excitement of those early days?

In part, the excitement came from a great explosion of new knowledge. At the scale of global geology, there was plate tectonics (wow!), and the first whispers of seismic stratigraphy. Locally, there was the thrill of discovering - in flash after flash of insight - how the North Sea came to be as it is. And in geophysics there was the digital revolution - magical processes that no one could explain without mathematics - improvements so fast that you could tell the year of a section just by looking at it.

Many factors fed the excitement.

One of these was the competition, and the secrecy. What had BP found? Who was that having lunch with Angus Beckett? What was the weird contraption on the back deck of the Western boat? Be careful to put that stuff in the safe; they say you can buy seismic lines by the yard in some shady pub in Victoria.

Another was the surprises. The sheer size of Groningen boggled our minds. We adjusted to a Permian play, and then were boggled again; we stood on ancient rocks in Scotland, and looked across to ancient rocks in Norway - and behold! there was a deep basin and a full geologic succession in between. And there were plays throughout the succession, from the Devonian to the Tertiary - even, would you believe, in the Chalk. What's more, it wasn't just gas - there was oil! (Whatever happened to all those promises to drink every barrel?) And not just oil, but oodles of oil. We were gobsmacked.

In geophysics too there were surprises. Some of the new processes worked unbelievably well, while others that should have been better were worse. Interpreters paid lip services to resolution, but actually preferred lolloping low-frequency reflections that were easy to pick. And a three-fold stack? No one will ever pay to shoot three times more than you need.

Another fact or feeding the excitement, in geophysics, was the headiness of survival.

The digital revolution was tough to master - a whole new way of working. Many geophysicists gave up, and went into chicken farming. But the rest of us held on, and enjoyed our skill, and prospered, and looked down on chicken farmers. (The chicken farmers laughed last, later.)

And, for those of us who were Brits, the excitement was fed by a certain tribal satisfaction.

In the early days, most of us had learned our trade from Okie geologists and Texan doodlebuggers and Louisianan rednecks. This gave us a fund of good stories; we pulled legs, and doubtless had ours pulled in return. But make no mistake - those guys were good. They were hoary with experience, and had a good practical way with them. Oil exploration was an American skill; the jargon was American, the literature was American, the equipment was American.

But after years of saluting the experts, there comes an itch. An itch to hear someone say: 'Well, that sure ain't the way we do it in Texas, but I guess it's OK.' The North Sea gave us the chance to prove our mettle. Not to the extent of feeling smug (learning goes on, for everyone), but at least to the extent of knowing that we made a significant contribution to the welfare of our tribe.

Before the North Sea, Britain was the sick man of Europe. Crippled by poor industrial management, myopic unions, overambitious social programmes and massive debt, Britain was in the hands of the receivers (that is, the IMF). The North Sea brought escape. For the government, revenues beyond the dreams of avarice. For the hundreds of thousands involved in the total effort, a place to broaden, and to relearn the lessons of commercial reality. And to us in the van of the charge the satisfactions of discovery and creative thought, the good feeling of hard work fulfilled.

Of course, we have learned to celebrate our achievement quietly, as in this little book. No one else knows. What history class is ever told that Britain was once saved by the oil industry? Or asked to write an essay speculating what social unrest would have torn the country if the Treasury had not had the money to pay the dole of 3 million unemployed?

But enough of that; let's talk about geophysics.

Because the success of the North Sea was the success of geophysics. Particularly in the oil province, where there were no onshore leads, the best geology in the world, by itself, could never have discovered the riches beneath that featureless sea. It was geophysics, and geophysics alone, that pointed the way to those riches.

Not that every seismic program was a success, by any means. In the early days, in particular, any structure seen was seen through bathroom glass. Geophysicists were called geofuzzies.

And therein lay another surprise. The North Sea emerged just as the seismic method was taking a great leap forward; quite fortuitously, the problem and the solution came together, at exactly the right time.

The early techniques were sufficient to show the largest structures, at least to modest depth. When we needed to see deeper, there came stacking. When we needed more detail, there came deconvolution. As we saw the importance of faulting, and salt movement, and overpressure, and gas indicators, there came migration, and velocities, and depth conversion, and true amplitudes. It was like a dance - the geological need and the seismic solution coming together, in step.

Even the geography yielding a happy coincidence. In the earliest days, when marine seismic techniques were at their crudest, the area being worked (offshore the Netherlands) happened to be one of the best seismic areas in the world; they used to say you could get good reflections with a cap. Each time the search expanded to a new area, even up into the difficult north, the seismic method was ready with the next improvement, to make it possible."

1. **Acquisition and Processing**

Fig. 5.1
BP (1964) North Sea survey on board 'Texin'. A charge is fired about 200 m astern of the ship.

Norman Hempstead takes up the story:

"Nineteen sixty four, the year that the PESGB was formed was also the year when the first digital recordings of seismic data in the North Sea were made. This was not entirely accidental; the North Sea was emerging as a likely major new hydrocarbon province after the discovery in 1959 of the Groningen gas field. The realisation, in the next year or so that this was a giant field led to seismic activity rapidly spreading offshore by 1962. And by 1964 both seismic and drilling exploration activity had advanced well into UK waters. The formation of a PESGB was inevitable.

By then the benefits of digital recording and processing had been demonstrated by Geophysical Service Inc. (GSI), initially in the USA, and the high level of seismic activity in the North Sea probably made it also inevitable that the digital method would be brought here. In fact the first digital recordings in the North Sea were made in May and June of that year. In that summer I was in the USA being introduced to this new magic method. An enthusiastic convert, I found myself a few months later assigned as an Area Geophysicist in London with a brief to promote the new technological development. It took time to mature and I had egg on my face many times in the next few months, when the actual result fell short of the magical expectation I had told a Client to expect! I recall cases where the fact that we could deconvolve a section after CDP stack could not make up for the fact that we had made a cobblers of stacking it! No fault of the digital approach, just that we had got the velocities wrong, but it can take a lot of explaining to a Chief Geophysicist who possibly thought one was a charlatan in the first place. You can't win 'em all; and I didn't. But gradually the increased dynamic range of digital recording and the power of digital computer processing proved themselves.

At that time CDP stacking itself was being used only selectively on North Sea surveys, although the technique was several years old. No doubt this was partly because the cost of multiple coverage was considerably more than that of single-fold but it was also because (whether analogue or digital) one did not always get the velocities right and results could be disappointing.

Apart from one GSI vessel equipped with a digital recorder, all of the seismic vessels in the North Sea in 1964 recorded in analogue formats and a number of analogue processing centres in London and elsewhere in Europe were involved in their processing. Fig. 5.2 is a view of such a centre which included a Multiple Analyser & Eliminator (MAE) - an analogue dereverberation device which was the brain-child of Milo Backus. The first production use of MAE worldwide had been on an Arabian Gulf survey processed in London in 1958, so the method was well established. Thousands of North Sea kilometres gave up the ghost, or rather the reverberations, to MAE's charms, well into the 1960's. Digital deconvolution was a big step forward when it came but these analogue devices had already taken a major step towards improving the resolution of marine seismic data prior to its introduction (see Fig. 5.3).

Fig. 5.2
Analogue processing centre showing Magnedisc (FM analogue recorder used for first production survey which used the MAE processor), Techno (an early AM analogue magnetic recording system) and the MAE dereverberation system.

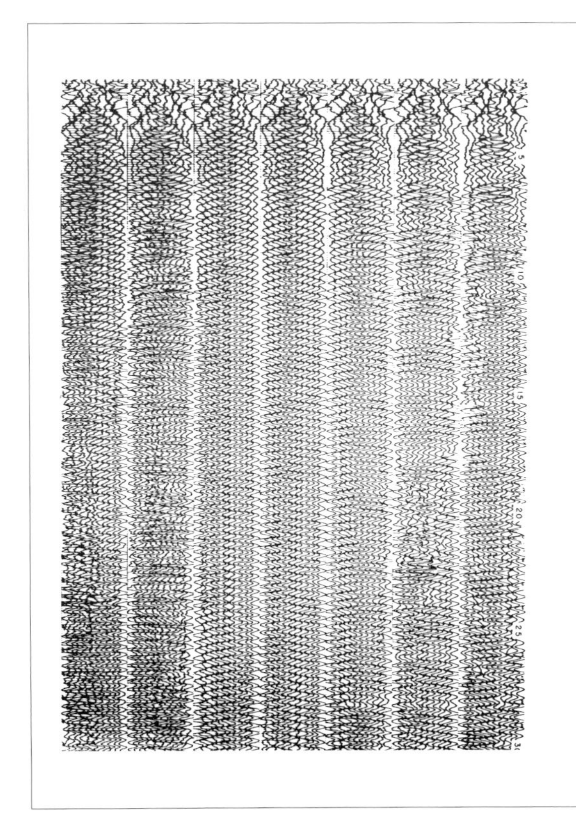

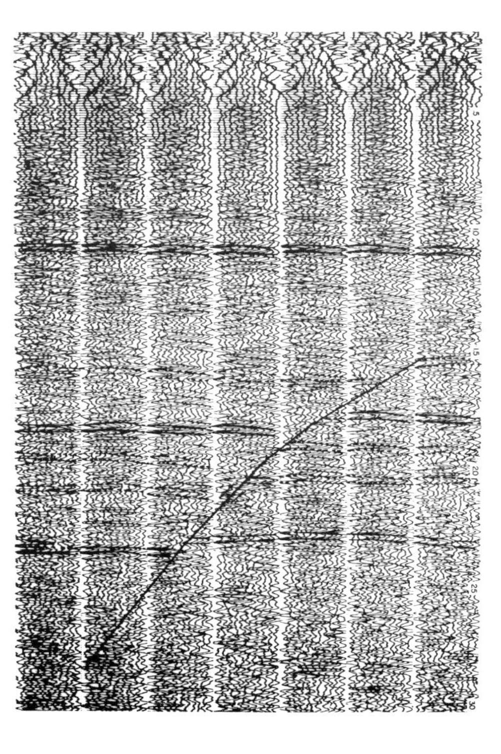

Fig. 5.3
Example of how effective analogue dereverberation could sometimes be, even in the early 1960s.
(i - Far Left)
Suite of marine records showing dominant Water reverberations before MAE processing
(ii - Left)
Suite of same marine records processed through MAE to remove water reverberations

Shell, in the Hague, had another dereverberation device, a wonderful machine, the heart of which looked like (and was) a gramophone turntable. This was the brain-child of a mad scientist and delightful character named George Sirks. But it really did the job. They don't make 'em like that any more - man or machine!

The first production digital seismic processing centre outside the USA was established in Croydon in April/May 1965 (see Fig. 5.4).

Fig. 5.4
An original "loop-tape" TIAC (Texas Instruments Automatic Computer) - this is a view in the centre which was installed in Croydon April/May 1965.

Thirty years later it is obvious that CDP stacking and digital data collection and processing were two of the tiny handful of major technological breakthroughs in the history of the seismic reflection method, but they did not come about in a sudden flash of light; they required a lot of diligent practice to bring them to the point where they could be relied on to work well essentially all the time.

In 1964 it was tough to record 3-fold CDP data and at the forefront of technology to record 6-fold, when this required chucking a primed 33 1/3- or 50-pound can of explosive overboard roughly every 45 seconds and required having several tons of the stuff on the back deck all the time.

Thirty years later when we routinely record perhaps 120-fold data or maybe 60-fold data on several streamers at the same time all this seems old hat, but a lot of water has passed under the bridges of a lot of seismic ships and huge investments of brains and money have been needed to achieve this.

Single-fold data were invariably recorded into split spreads, in order to provide time ties on the end traces from record to record when character correlation of reflections is ambiguous, but with multiple coverage it became more practical to correlate reflections between consecutive records when shooting offend. Fig. 5.5 shows a line which was recorded digitally in 1964 both split and off-end for comparison. Although only 3-fold data, the off-end section shows better multiple attenuation and some pre-salt events are more continuous as a result.

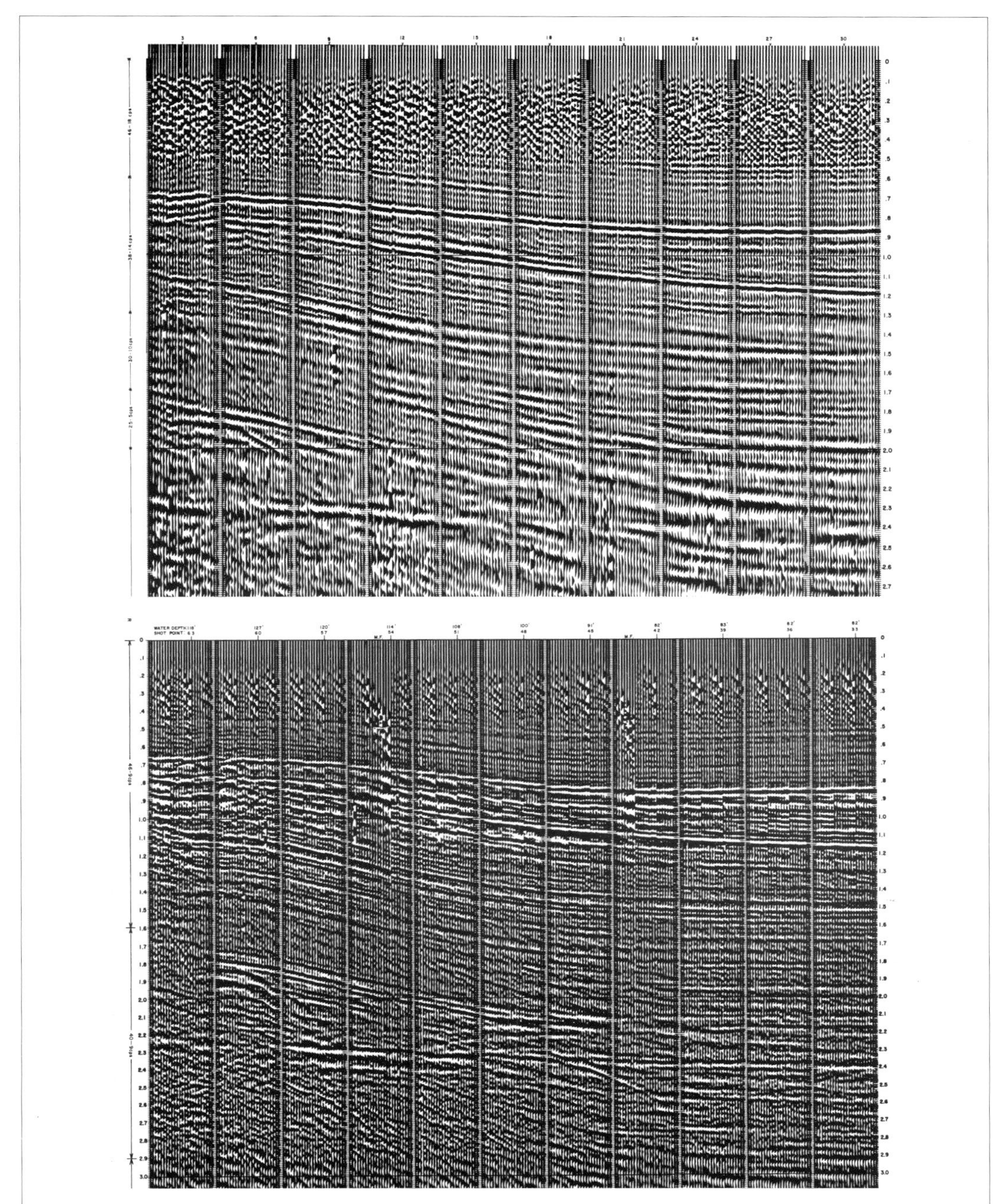

Fig 5.5
1964 North Sea line. Note the improved definition on the off-end spread of events below the salt pillow around 2.3 seconds.
(i - Top)
Split spread
(ii - Bottom)
Off-end spread

1964 also had big memories for Bob Dyk - in fact his first time introduction to the North Sea:

"It was on June 23rd, my wife's fiftieth birthday that I sailed from Middlesborough on a seismic boat heading for a five day cruise in search of a gas prospect or two. We finally completed our 'five day' programme on day 12. In that period, I gained a lot of valuable first hand experience in the unique North Sea operational problems which helped me in later years. The North Sea proved to be just as advertised even in mid-summer, a miserable, nasty, violent place to work. The weather changes were consistent, quickly varying from bad to worse - back to bad. This was the main cause of the delays in completing the programme within the estimated five day period. The seismic boat was a converted frigate, as many such boats were at that time. They came cheap for obvious reasons if you'd ever sailed on one. I found living on one under North Sea conditions was a sickening experience demanding quick and frequent access to the leeward rail. The number two holdup arose from having to use the only available positioning system, that provided by Decca. It was only functional in daylight hours and every morning you first had to try to find where you were; then try to get to where you should be; and hope you were actually there when you started work. This created innumerable problems when tying or continuing lines shot the previous day.

Bad weather meant abject boredom. The ship's library consisted mainly of accumulated 'Penthouse' and 'Playboy' magazines, cowboy comics, books about when the west was wild; the film library, more of the same. It was surprising how quickly the glamour of the centrefold vanished when overexposed thereto.

The recording system was a 'state-of-the-art' analogue system which stored the data on tape but also spewed out yards of paper records. If you knew how to and had the time, you could undertake shipboard mapping of the daily data output and not have to wait on the delivery of the onshore processed analogue tapes. So when we finally went ashore we had a complete set of interpretations mapped on the areas surveyed. It was a lucky thing we had these, as the day of the 'big event' was very close. That day was the closing date for the applications for production licences in the UK portion of the North Sea".

Following on from the First Round, 1965 was a busy year for seismic acquisition. Norman Hempstead writes:

"The digital test lines recorded in the North Sea in 1964 were processed in Dallas during the winter of 1964-65 and prepared the way for digital recording in 1965, when quite a number of North Sea surveys were recorded digitally and many examples of processed data became available. See Fig. 5.6, which shows a sample of data from a production digital survey from the North Sea in 1965.

Fig. 5.6 shows detail from a seismic section through a processing sequence; from single-fold data after preliminary processing such as amplitude recovery and normal moveout (Fig. 5.6 (i)); a 6-fold stack of these data (Fig. 5.6 (ii)); the same single-fold records after deconvolution (Fig. 5.6 (iii)); and the 6-fold stacked section with deconvolution (Fig. 5.6 (iv)). The value of 600% stacking and of deconvolution are both well illustrated.

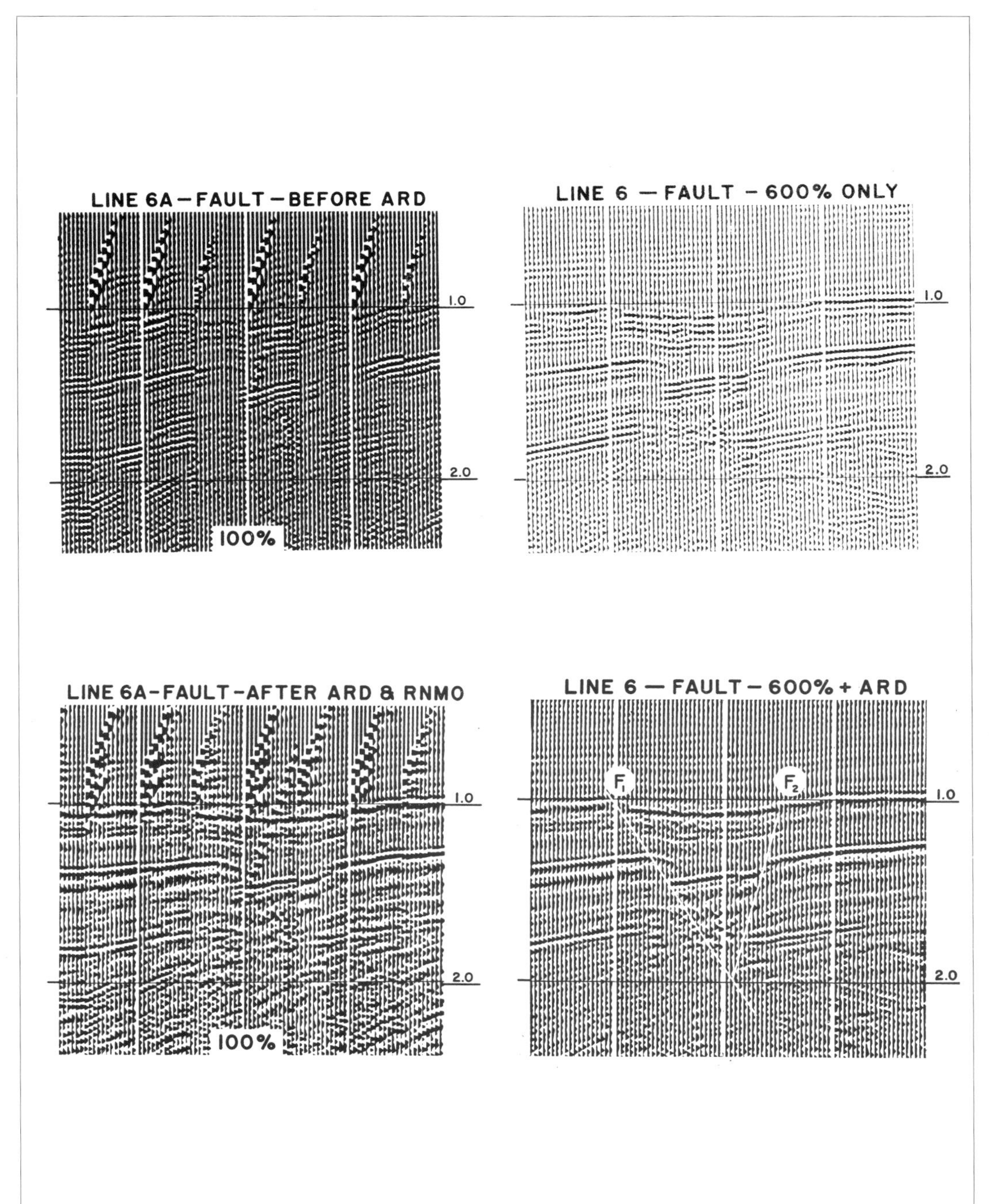

Fig. 5.6 Processing sequence illustrating the value of deconvolution and of 600% CDP coverage.
(i - Top Left) *Single-fold data without deconvolution.*
(ii - Top Right) *Six-fold data without deconvolution.*
(iii - Bottom Left) *Single-fold data after deconvolution.*
(iv - Bottom Right) *Six-fold data after deconvolution.*

Progressive improvements due to the use of longer streamers, more recording channels and groups per streamer, higher CDP fold and continual improvements in the flexibility of digital processes and (especially) in the general level of expertise in their application led to a progressive increase in the resolution of the seismic section".

It was not to be much longer, however, before dynamite as a marine source was replaced by a suite of environmentally friendlier (and usually cheaper) alternatives (see later). Philip Nelson recalls, in 1967, Shell Expro's last true dynamite line in the North Sea...... :

"In January 1967, when I joined Shell UK Exploration and Production Ltd - a separate company in those days - the first final stacks of a large 1966 survey in The Central Graben were trickling into the office in Shell Centre. These lines, all of which had been shot with the luxury of 6-fold stacking and the 'new' digital technology, were considered a big advance on the pre-existing analogue dynamite data, which ranged from the 1962 single coverage, split-spread, two boat lines, to the 4-fold, end-on, single boat lines of 1964, stacked optically, side-by-side on Shell's Robinson Machine in the Hague.

I remember Norman Hempstead, then the key link man of GSI (remember them?), personally and with great pride presenting some of the more amazing profiles of the 1966 survey.

The six seconds record length was proving its worth deep in the graben, but, to the west, it seemed a bit of an overkill, since nothing but noise could be seen below the base Zechstein at two seconds or less. In response to the cynicism expressed by Colin Kirkpatrick, at that time Shell Expro's Chief Geophysicist and my boss, Norman employed a neat trick of 'profile enhancement'. This involved folding under the bottom four seconds or so of the profile, thereby concentrating attention on only that part containing usable data.

Thus duly convinced that his decision to commit to this extensive survey in 1966 had been the right one, Colin's immediate reaction was, 'OK, so how about 12-fold?'. Norman thought for a moment, and, never one to say 'No', agreed that a trial 12-fold line could be shot. And, 'for the good of my soul', I was instructed by Colin to join the boat as observer - or client rep'.

A couple of weeks and a train ride to Middlesborough later, I met Mal Caswell (then with GSI) on the dockside, and we boarded the Anø Lindinger (see Fig. 5.7) for what was to prove to be Shell Expro's last true dynamite line in the North Sea. Airguns were already 'popping' on trial in the Gulf of Mexico and, as we were to find out, 12-fold dynamite was pushing that technology to the absolute limit in the harsh conditions of the North Sea.

Fig. 5.7
GSI's seismic vessel Anø Lindinger at the quayside in Teesport, Middlesborough. Phil Nelson (the author) inspects the diminutive size of the ship.

Before coming up on station for the first shot, the cable was streamed, and as many charges as possible - 'bombs' as they were affectionately called - were brought up to the shooting deck from deep in the bowels of the ship. 'The only safe way to do this,' I remember the shooter saying, 'is to have lots and lots of 'bombs', ready to go.' (see Fig. 5.8). Looking at the sea of canisters around our feet, I could not help wondering if we would know anything about it, if just one of those 33 lb ultra high energy baked bean tins proved 'ready to go' prematurely. Fortunately, in the event, we had no cause to test that conjecture.

Fig. 5.8
Port side of the shooting deck of the Anø Lindinger. Knee-deep in high explosive, the shooter inspects the firing line.

Shooting on the first day (daylight only at that time) went reasonably well, but it was obvious that the shooting cycle - a shot every 32 seconds - was pushing the system pretty hard (see Fig. 5.9). On the second day, with only half the line completed on day one, we were not so lucky with the weather. Wind and sea had roughed up overnight, but it was considered possible to continue in spite of the increased noise, as long as the ship-to-streamer offset was increased. So, with a longer lead-in, and correspondingly longer shooting lines (one on each side, port and starboard), work started on the second half of the line.

Fig. 5.9
Waterspout from a shot fired at the correct depth in good weather conditions.

The conditions slowly but surely deteriorated, and it became increasingly difficult to control shot depth in order to avoid either bubble-pulse or blow out. We experienced several of each; the bubble pulses slamming the hull of the ship as double sledge-hammer blows, and the blow-outs occasionally pumping backwash right through the ship to the instrument room. As the weather got worse the observers called for an even greater ship-to-streamer offset in a vain attempt to minimise ship and cable noise.

Misfire!

The two shooting lines were paid out accordingly, and, in the end, the charges were exploding some 1,000ft astern of the ship, as I recall. Shooting from the starboard line, we continued in this mode for a while until inevitably, 'Misfire!' After four misfires in succession, the call came down to start shooting on the port line. Then came the daunting prospect of hauling in the starboard line to investigate the cause of the misfires. The combination of the ship's forward speed, the massive offset to the shots and streamer, and the rate of progress of each 'bomb' down the shooting line from launch to hook, meant that at any time there were no less than four 'bombs' on the line, while a fifth was poised in a cradle on the ship's gunwale prior to launching. The prospect of hauling four unexploded 'bombs' close to the ship's hull as we brought in the offending shooting line was one that temporarily dispelled all feelings of sea-sickness.

Imagine our relief when, with knuckles whitening and faces turning blue from holding our breath, we peered into the water to see just a bare brass hook snaking along in the wake of the shooting line.

And to a Question in The House, the then Minister of Agriculture, Fisheries and Food was able to assure Honourable Members that there were no unexploded charges on the sea-bed of the North Sea.

They were there alright, but, having been punctured with a marlin spike, the theory was they would be rendered inert in a matter of days. And so far that theory has proved to be robust."

Norman Hempstead documents the advent of non-dynamite sources - particularly airguns - which of course are still very much with us today:

"Probably the most important next step forward (not in the sudden breakthrough category because it was a more gradual progression, but of enormous long term importance) was the introduction of non-dynamite sources.

Various non-dynamite marine sources were developed, predominantly during the 1960s. Of these, several were successful and were used extensively for a decade or two worldwide. Amongst those which achieved many successful surveys in the NorthSea were (in alphabetical order):

Airgun (in many versions); *Aquapulse* (a version of the Esso Sleeve Exploder); *Esso Sleeve Exploder; Flexotir; Maxipulse; Sodera* (Watergun); *Vaporchoc.*

Of these, the source which through many transitions has developed to become the most widely used worldwide is the airgun, and its history is interesting since it shows how a good idea can develop given imagination and perseverance.

In the early 1960's Bolt airguns were being used for such applications as harbour bottom surveys. In 1965-6, GSI extended their use to deep exploration targets. Ten Bolt airguns, each with an air chamber capacity of 10 cubic inches, were mounted on a shallow draft barge and this system was used for a deep survey in the Corpus Christi Bay in the Gulf of Mexico. By summing many pops of a number of guns popping synchronously, it was expected to obtain deep penetration although the output from one pop of a single gun has low energy.

Fig. 5.10 shows a picture of this barge. Each gun was mounted on a separate gantry arm so that the air supply to that gun could be shut off and the gun swung onboard for repairs. As I remember, one or more guns would be on deck most of the time during the working day while the airgun mechanic frantically replaced O-rings or solenoids or fixed some other problem, hopefully before another gun failed and had to be hauled in for attention.

Fig. 5.10
First use of airguns for deep seismic survey developed on this barge for use in Corpus Christi Bay in 1966.

When all of the guns had equal sized air chambers (10 cubic inches) the signature of the pulse was very much elongated due to the oscillation of the bubble. In the autumn of 1966 I spent a most enjoyable weekend on this crew at Aransas Pass, on the Texas Gulf Coast, eating some of the most magnificent but cheapest seafood I have ever encountered, while we tested an idea proposed by Ben Giles of using an array of guns with different air chamber capacities.

The oscillation frequencies of the bubbles from guns of different reservoir volumes varied so that the bubble energy was effectively cancelled out and the 'tuned airgun array' was born. The results of this experimental system are illustrated in Fig. 5.11. Strong events are seen to the bottom of the section at 5.0 seconds.

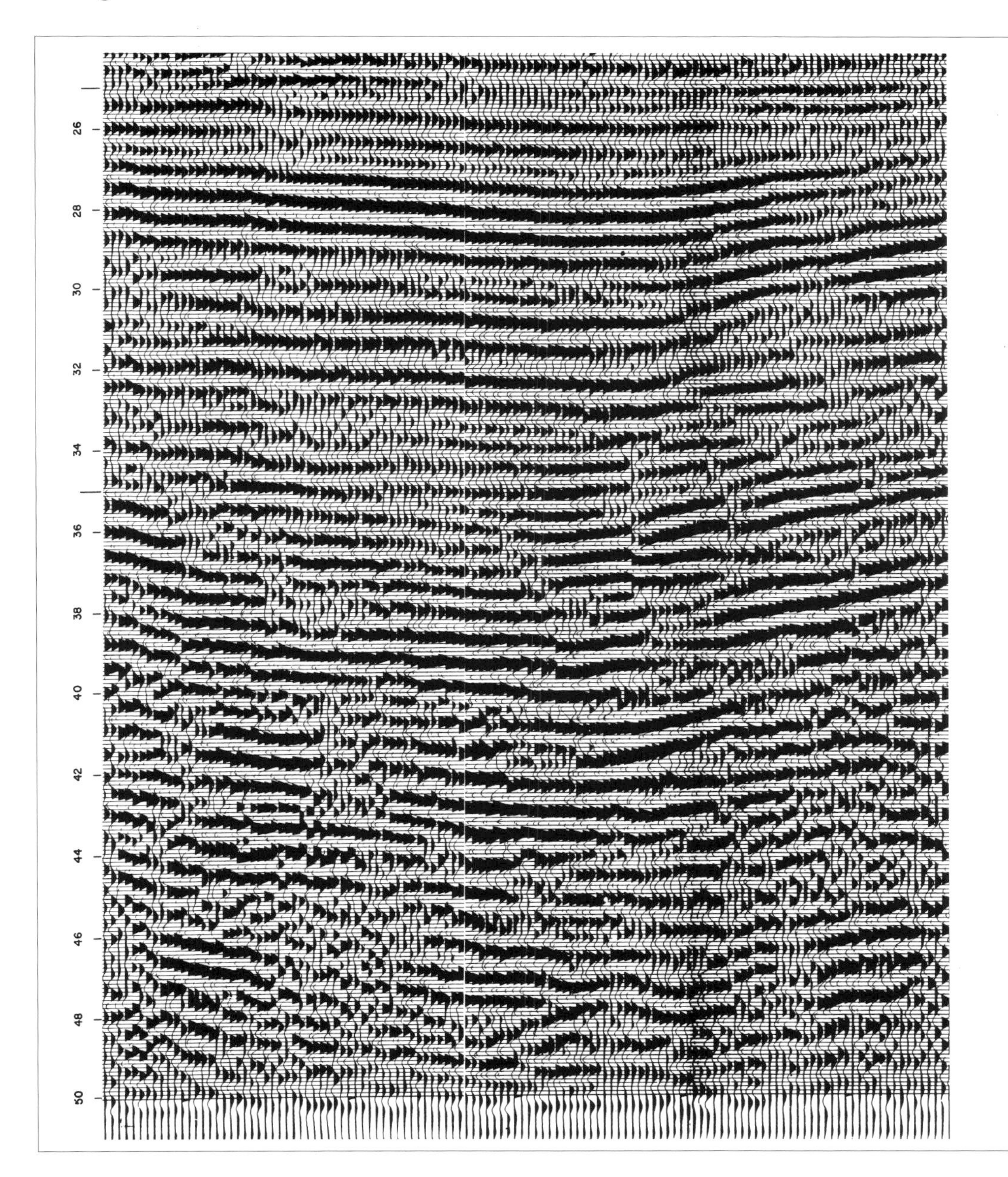

Fig. 5.11
Segment of an airgun section from the Corpus Christi barge operation using (comparatively embryonic) ‘“tuned array” of airguns, showing strong data down to 5.0 seconds.

In this relatively static shallow water mode the system was very effective. Now to extend the idea to a continuous-tow deep-water marine operation. Some weeks later found us in the Santa Barbara Channel with some airguns built in the Texas Instruments workshops to a modified design intended to overcome the high failure rate. After about 72 hours (fortunately in idyllic weather) man-handling 16 guns strung together by steel ropes in and out of the water without benefit of any winch gear, we had not succeeded in recording enough successive pops without autofires to produce a CDP stacked section. That week end was a good way to keep fit but there was a bit more design work to do. Back to the workshop!

The remaining problems were soon sorted out and the era of the tuned array continuous tow airgun source was established.

It was first introduced into North Sea operations in 1967 and for the next few years it, Aquapulse (based on the Esso Sleeve Exploder), Flexotir and various other

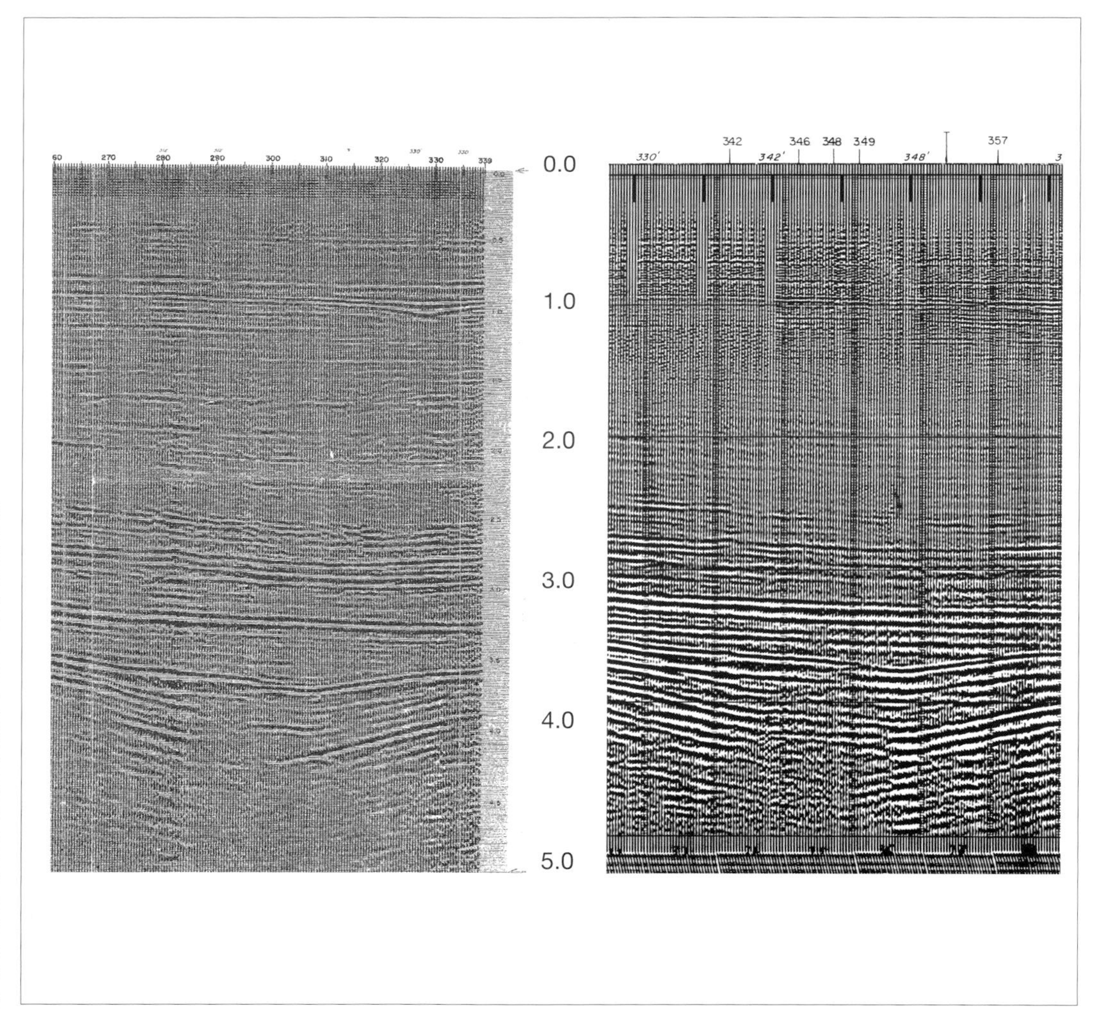

Fig. 5.12
Early North Sea data: Airgun and dynamite comparison recorded in 1967.
(i - Left)
Dynamite data - recorded and processed 12 - fold CDP stack
(ii Right)
Airgun data - recorded 24 - fold processed 4 - fold vertical stack followed by 6 - fold CDP stack

sources competed fiercely against conventional dynamite and then progressively against each other to capture the market with an environmentally-friendly source.

It is well said that 'there is no such thing as a free lunch'. Seismic crews, accustomed to eat well off the fish left floating belly up astern seismic ships using dynamite were said to eat less well with the advent of environmentally-friendly sources. Airguns actually titillated the fishes' sexual appetites, no doubt increasing their population, but it did not kill them, so the poor doodlebuggers went hungry. So I was told, but that was 'telling it to the Marines' so it may not be one hundred percent true.

There have been many changes in the design of airguns and airgun arrays since that time and their efficiency and the resolution obtainable by their use has progressed a long way, but this is a typical example of the kind of dogged perseverance rather than inspirational breakthrough which has accounted for most of the progress from the first one-trace reflection seismogram recorded in 1926 to the reflection surveys of today.

One other really important development in seismic reflection technology which was initiated during the first 15 years of the PESGB's life was the introduction of 3D seismic surveying. This was certainly a breakthrough, though like the others it did not happen all at once but required a great deal of diligence and perseverance before it became well established.

The first 3D survey in the North Sea was performed speculatively by GSI in October 1975 as a means of demonstrating the principle in order to impact North Sea activity in 1976. It was performed in somewhat adverse conditions in the late season and somewhat 'on the cheap' - that is to say, with a line spacing of 200 metres. This sampling was not adequate for optimum resolution of the geology but the processed results provided clear indications of the potential of 3D. Fig. 5.13 shows a comparison of a CDP stack line from this survey and a 3D migrated profile beneath the same surface traverse.

Compared with the resolution routinely achieved by 3D surveys today this is not particularly impressive, but these data were used to good effect in promoting the use of the 3D technique in the North Sea in 1976.

It took several years of gradual improvement in the performance of 3D surveys for them to become universally accepted as a necessary exploration and exploitation tool.

But the technique has never looked back and there is probably no producing oil or gas field in the North Sea today which has escaped the attention of at least one 3D survey.

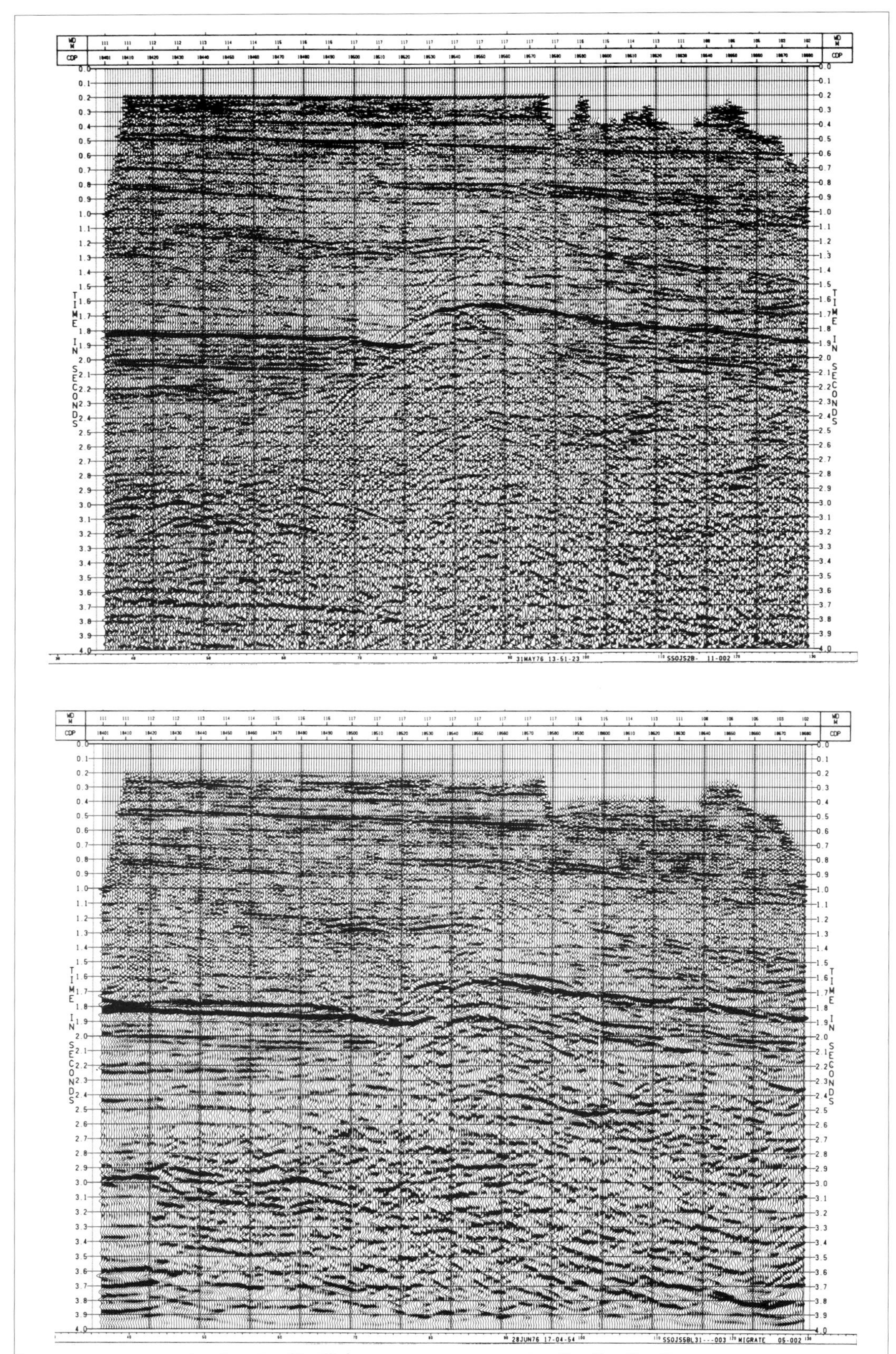

Fig. 5.13
Illustration of capability of 3D v 2D data - from the first 3D survey shot in the North Sea in October 1975.
(i - Top)
Bin stacked data (max fold 96) before migration.
(ii - Bottom)
3D migrated data along same stacktrack.

When one considers the increase in technological effort over the years, from 24 trace single fold or 3-fold recording in 1964 to 48 and sometimes 96 trace 24 or 48 fold in 1979, accompanied by a considerable increase in the processing complexity of what was considered a standard sequence, it is just as well that computers have become massively faster and processes markedly more efficient with time.

In 1964, I remember a list price for performing a deconvolution with a 55-point operator on a 5-second 24-trace record at 1 millisecond sampling was $35, i.e. £12. That would have been roughly equivalent to £50 in 1979 and to £120 in 1994.

In 1979 £50 would probably have bought a kilometre or two of data processed through a typical sequence of pre-stack preparation, 4800% CMP stack, post-stack conditioning, migration and display for 2400-metre, 96 trace data.

If you spent £120 per kilometre in 1994 you would get all the processing you could imagine and a drilling rig would be thrown in as a sweetener to secure the contract!"

A final word, perhaps, on seismic costs comes from statistics quoted by Peter Hinde:

"It is estimated that a total of £10,000,000 has been spent on seismic exploration of the North Sea during the three summers of 1963, 1964 and 1965. Countless duplicate miles must have been shot by the same seismic exploration company working for different clients. At an average cost of about £130 per mile it may be argued that a lot of money has been wasted. And fish killed."

Fig. 5.14
This shows a BP North Sea survey on board the 'Texin'. The cans of high explosives are clearly visible - on deck!

Before we take our discussion further and look at the evolution of early seismic interpretations, it is worth remembering the other side of operational geophysics: check shots or well shoots. Philip Nelson (following on from his experiences with Shell's last dynamite line) recalls his next North Sea assignment:

"My next excursion offshore, again 'for the good of my soul', was to a well-shoot in the Southern Gas Province. By this time, Spring 1967, Leman and Inde were both ripe for development and the subject of vigorous, occasionally outrageous, unitisation discussions between Shell/Esso and the Amoco Group. In this context of a rapidly maturing play, the well-shoot of an Inde appraisal well was considered purely routine, but still a useful learning experience for one such as myself, only 18 months into an oil industry career.

'What you will observe,' said Colin Kirkpatrick, 'is the shooting boat circling the rig, firing a charge each time it passes one of two marker buoys, offset some 150 ft or so on opposite sides of the rig. The well geophone will be pulled up the hole between each pair of shots. It's all routine stuff', he went on, 'and should be easily accomplished in one day. But pack a toothbrush, just in case'.

In those days, the British Airways helipad was right outside Shell Expro's offices in Lowestoft. And reaching Lowestoft by train presented no problems either, so a couple of hours out of London I met up with the observer from SSL (remember them, too?), and we boarded the chopper. Safety procedures ('At the insistence of the Board of Trade,' explained the chief pilot) were basic, but included the sort of instructions meted out to fare-paying passengers in today's commercial airlines. Subjects as profound as how to inflate your life jacket and use the whistle to attract attention were covered, but no special attire was demanded or provided, and neither of us, the only two passengers on that flight, had been on any survival course. Did such things exist in early 1967?

'As soon as we're airborne,' continued the skipper, 'feel free to come up to the flight deck for a chat.' Yes, those were the days, and during the ensuing 'chat', made possible by donning the spare headset kindly proffered by the co-pilot, I learned (amongst other things) about the fundamental difference between aeroplanes and helicopters. 'Always remember,' said the skipper, 'while an aeroplane is trying to fly, a helicopter is actually trying to crash. You've got to watch them constantly.' And as if in confirmation, he made frequent nudge adjustments of the four-way trim control on the joy-stick.

Conditions were excellent as we touched down on the helipad of Transocean II (Fig. 5.15), a six-legged jack-up, and on stepping out of the chopper, I was immediately aware of the rig's slight motion, monitored, I later discovered by two 'earthquake' seismometers deep within the superstructure of the rig. But before being shown the seismometers, my enquiry was unashamedly confirmed by the tool-pusher, who explained that the teeth on the rack and pinion lifting gear were badly worn, and that this was definitely the last well before an extensive refit in a Dutch yard. Yes, this was a fixed platform, but a gently and distinctly rocking one, nonetheless (Fig. 5.16).

Fig. 5.15
*Chopper landing on the helipad of'Transocean II'. Maybe **this** flight brought the senior op's man from Shell in The Hague!*

Fig. 5.16
Transocean II at night. The crane's block in the foreground is not out of focus. It is blurred in this time exposure because it is gently swaying in response to the rig's constant rocking motion.

The open hole section to be shot was stable, with mud of the appropriate weight circulating slowly. The shooting boat arrived, and the drill string was withdrawn and stacked in the derrick. It turned out that this was SSL's No 2 shooting boat, the No 1 evidently busy further north on another well. Both these boats were merely 'converted' trawlers, though the 'conversions' seemed to have involved little more than replacing fish with dynamite, caps and turkey bags - large, orange, inflatable plastic bags, used to suspend charges at the correct depth.

Wandering markers

When the shooting boat started laying out the marker buoys, the inexperienced crew - the No 2 boat was rarely used, such was the pace of drilling at that time - failed to recognise the strength of the tidal current in these shallow waters, and made the lines too short. The result was that by the time the boat was 'on station' to fire the first shot, the buoy had drifted down on the rig, and was only a matter of yards away when the shot went off. The unusually loud thud startled everyone on the rig, and we rushed to the guard rail to see the shooting boat almost vertically beneath us bobbing dangerously close to the rig's legs. This was just the beginning of what turned out to be a chapter of incidents, accidents being too strong a word, since miraculously nobody was hurt though much time was lost (24 hours in fact).

After regaining his composure enough to inspect the record, the SSL observer then reported malfunction of the amplifier. He needed some special tools, as I remember, which were mysteriously in a tool-box on the shooting boat. We later discovered that there was a spare amplifier on the shooting boat, too. In a radio exchange with those on board the boat, instructions were given to sort out the problem of the drifting marker buoys and at the same time to come alongside the rig, or nearly alongside, and put the tool-box in a net to be hauled aboard the rig by one of the cranes. On this occasion, the manoeuvre was completed successfully and the observer turned to the task of putting the electronics back in running order.

The circuitry was pretty basic, the boards bristling with the usual crop of resistors, capacitors and transistors to be found growing in such places at that time, since 'chips' were not much more than a gleam on the horizon. As might have been expected, under pressure from the lanky Texan tool-pusher to 'get his arse into gear', the hapless SSL man accidentally drilled right through a key capacitor in his efforts to make a new mounting hole in one of the amplifier boards. This was not good news, but neither were the amazing feats of seamanship being performed by shooting boat No 2, apparently unable to lay a marker buoy and make it stick. It seemed as though Father Neptune was having a right regal chuckle at the crew's expense, enjoying himself so much that in the end the tool-pusher called a halt to proceedings, saying that the casing would have to be run. There was, after all, a goodly section of gas-bearing Rotliegend at the bottom of the well, and the hole could only be stood open for so long. At this point Colin Kirkpatrick's wise advice to pack a toothbrush took on a new significance, as I was to spend four days and three nights on that rig in the end.

Overnight the hole was conditioned by re-running the drill-string, circulating, and pulling out again; a round trip. Running the casing began the following morning, and, counting myself lucky to witness what would otherwise have happened after our departure, I took an active interest in the proceedings. The casing stands were assembled on the pipe deck, then hauled up the ramp to the derrick floor before being connected and lowered, a stand at a time, into the well. The crew had rigged a thin wire-line running from the derrick floor back down to the pipe deck. The casing thread protectors (large rubber washers equipped with a metal hook) were hung on this line to send them back to the pipe deck after the casing stands had negotiated the ramp and been connected to the previously run casing hanging in the slips.

Some time during the day, as I was crossing the pipe deck, I suddenly became aware of a couple of roughnecks gesticulating wildly and pointing skywards above my head. Looking up, I saw the thin wire-line tighten like a great guitar string, as the crane driver, oblivious of the fact that it was caught in his hook, continued to wind the hoop upwards in preparation for a lift from some other part of the rig.

Fig. 5.17 Looking down on the ramp leading from pipe deck to derrick floor on Transocean II. The wire snapped by the craneman can be seen hanging limply from the top of the ramp.

Confined to barracks

Sensing the inevitable, yet hoping to escape the whiplash of the snapping wire, I covered my head with my arms and hot-footed it towards the far end of the pipe deck. All was well and nobody got lashed, but my luck ran out, nonetheless. Unknown to me, a very senior operations manager from Shell in The Hague had landed from one of the several choppers that had come and gone since our arrival, and was witness to the near-miss from a window overlooking the pipe deck (Fig. 5.17).

Perhaps it was my unusually swift reaction that caught his attention, perhaps a real roughneck would simply have stood and gaped, but whatever it was he wanted to know, 'Who the devil is that?' On being told that it was an office wallah from London, and, moreover, an office wallah somehow involved with the frustratingly unfinished business of the well-shoot that had caused so much trouble the previous day, he issued instructions that I was to be confined to barracks for the rest of the casing running. This seemed incredibly rough justice on the only person on deck to take immediate and effective action at the time of the incident. Worse than that one of the galley stewards even started muttering the word 'Jonah'.

Conditions were still fine with a flat calm sea, when, with casing safely cemented in the hole, I was allowed out the following morning to assist with the continuation of the well- shoot. Although the shooting boat seemed to have mastered the knack of getting marker buoys to stay put, they had run into fresh difficulties related to getting charges to behave the same way. We watched as, incredibly, a charge broke free of whatever tenuous restraints had been imposed on it by the shooter (no doubt a highly skilled and experienced trawlerman, who would never willingly have said Goodbye to a full net), and disappeared in the direction of the Dutch coast. In spite of repeated radio calls from the rig notifying those on board the boat of the escaping charge and the implications thereof, the turkey bag was last seen disappearing into the haze on the south-eastern horizon. And this unexploded charge was not even on the sea bed.

Adding to the problems on the shooting boat, the rig-borne electronics were still very sick. After several vain attempts to breathe life into the amplifier that had caused so much trouble on the first day, the SSL observer admitted defeat and decided to bring the spare amplifier onto the rig from the shooting boat. Again, instructions were issued by radio to the boat, and again the boat swung alongside with the amplifier in its transit case resting in a net on the foredeck near the mast.

The craneman, unsighted by the rig's guard rail because of the proximity of the boat, lowered the hook to the directions of the tool-pusher. The boat was gently heaving in the swell as the crew on her foredeck engaged the hook in the net's strops, and the signal was given to start lifting. Soon after becoming airborne the net tangled with the cross-trees of the boat's mast, and had it not been for the strident voice of

Fig. 5.18
The crew on the shooting boat, now dangerously close to the rig's legs, struggle to bring the empty net on board, prior to transferring equipment to the rig.

the tool-pusher yelling in unprintable Texan tones to the craneman to let go, a second later the weight of the shooting boat would have been taken by the crane, and the crane's derrick would probably have snapped (Fig. 5.18). That could have been very nasty indeed, because several of us were standing directly underneath. While a snapping wire is one thing, a collapsing crane is something altogether different.

The last straw

This, as I remember it, was the last straw, and I don't think the well-shoot was ever completed. SSL's No 2 crew had caused quite enough trouble for one very irate Texan tool-pusher, who made it clear that the safety of his gently rocking rig was his principal concern, and that he'd definitely had enough. In any case it was only an appraisal well, and the identification of the principal horizons was never in doubt. So we made preparations for the flight ashore.

It was an almost full flight on the trip back to Lowestoft, and I remember the wife of one of the men going on days-off standing at the edge of the helipad as we touched down. The sight of a woman after four days in the North Sea was quite exhilarating, and I wondered why we hadn't missed them during the two years in the Antarctic prior to joining Shell."

2. **Interpretation**

James Hornabrook, from his papers in Petroleum International Journal (1974) provides a case history from the West Sole gasfield illustrating how interpretational geophysics was refined and modified in those early years. Not surprisingly, in this area of major halokinesis (salt movement), the evolution of depth conversion techniques proved one of the most critical parameters affecting increased accuracy and confidence of structure:

"The very first hydrocarbon find in the North Sea was the West Sole gasfield, discovered by BP in 1965. Early offshore seismic work had necessarily to rely to a great extent on the results obtained on land, mainly Holland. It soon became apparent that conditions were not necessarily the same offshore.

First seismic data was recorded in the West Sole area in 1962. This used 50-lb dynamite charges shot single cover into a straddle spread of 400 m each side of the shot. The analogue tapes recorded were plagued with heavy ringing and very strong multiples. Seismic sections produced were almost unreadable at all but the very shallow levels.

Despite the general poor quality of the data it was clear that the Zechstein evaporite series extended across the North Sea within a few miles of the English coast.

The reflection from the top of the Zechstein salt is easily recognised as being immediately above a series of very pronounced broad diffraction patterns. This is a diagnostic feature of the Permian salt reflection over most of the southern North Sea, and is probably caused by diffraction from the edges of fractured rafts of the brittle Z3 anhydrite, usually present near the top of the salt section.

Although there were various potential hydrocarbon-bearing targets in the North Sea, the initial search in the south was for duplication of the conditions present at Groningen, in Holland, where several thousand feet of Upper Permian (Zechstein) salt form the cap to the gas reservoir of high porosity Lower Permian (Rotliegend) sand. The presence of all these conditions cannot be determined by reflection seismology alone.

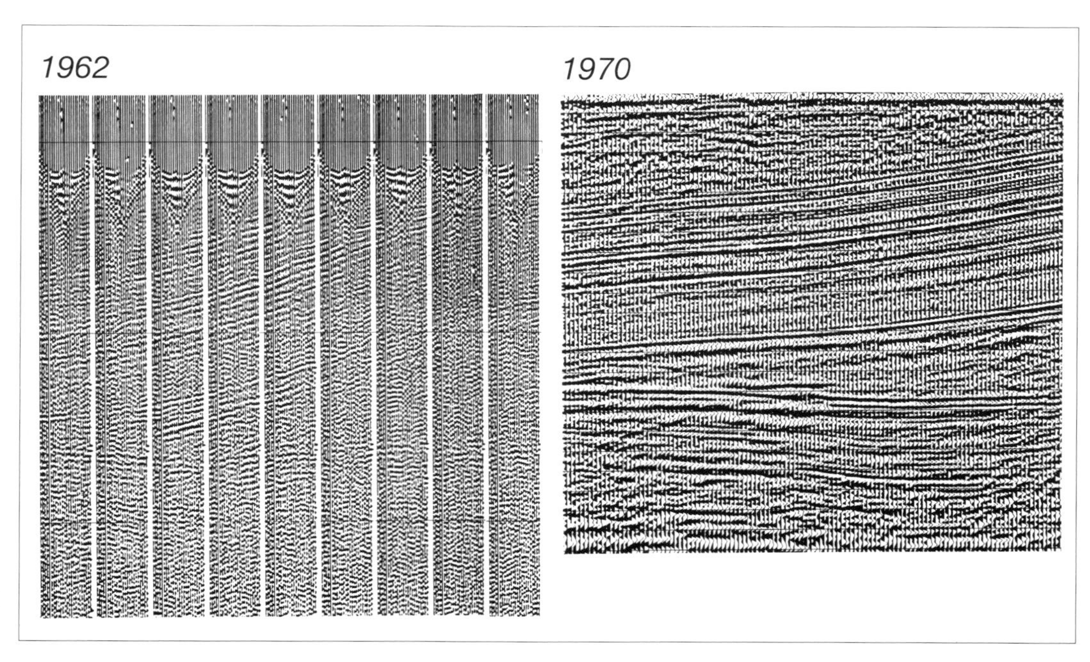

Fig. 5.19
Improvements in seismic quality.

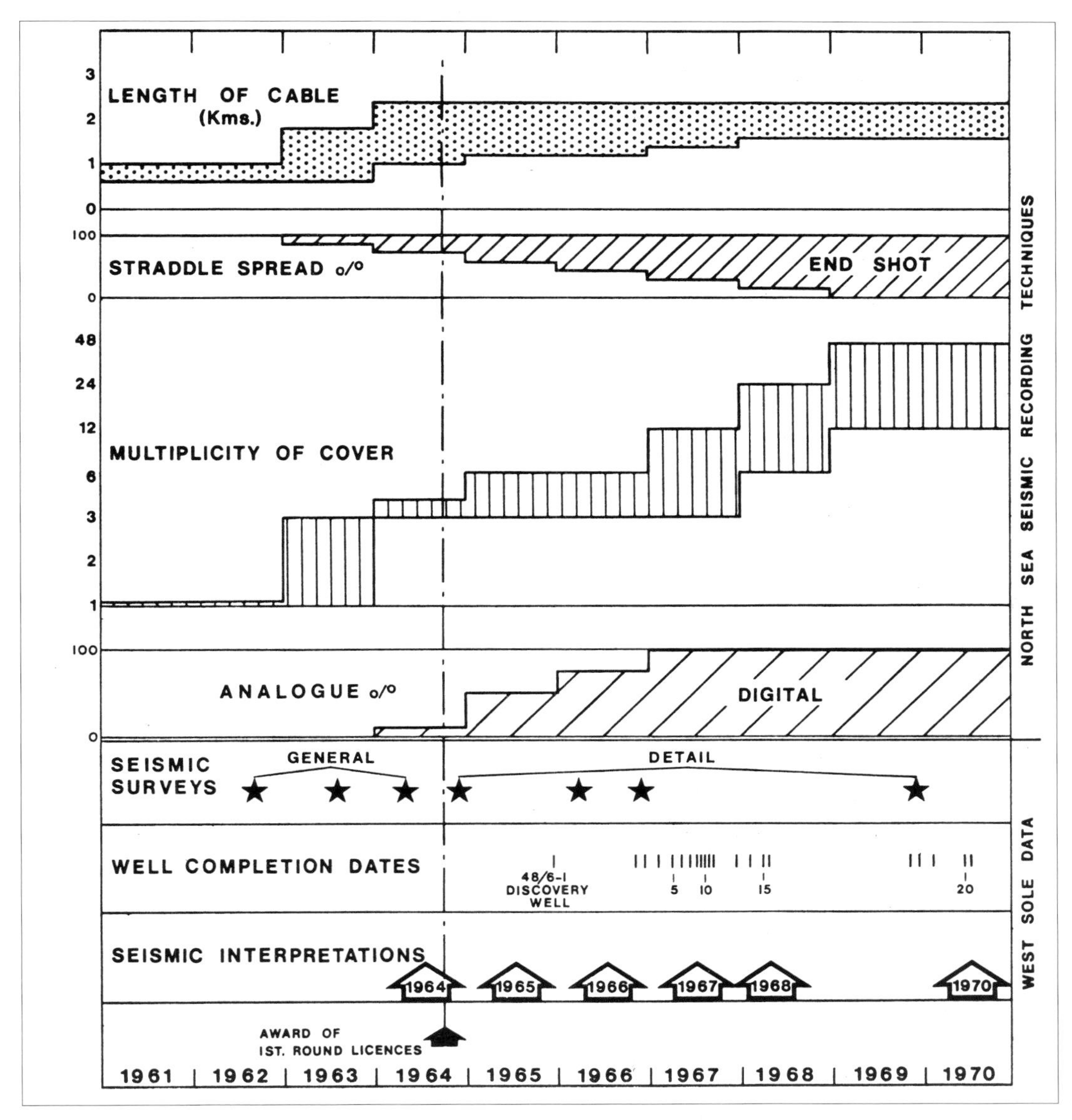

Fig. 5.20
West Sole data summary.

In the seismic surveys of 1963 and 1964 the base Zechstein anhydrite was the deepest reflector that could be readily identified. The existence of the Rotliegend sand and underlying Coal Measures could only be postulated.

The principal seismic objective was that of finding closed base Zechstein structures, but it proved very difficult to achieve this with the data available in 1962. Subsequently seismic methods developed rapidly and by the mid 1970s it was possible to read the basal Zechstein anhydrite reflection with considerable confidence and precision. The two lines in Fig. 5.19 demonstrate the improvement in seismic quality due to improved recording and processing techniques summarised in Fig. 5.20.

In some parts of the southern North Sea, reliable reflections could be obtained from several horizons. Studying the scanty data obtained from the velocity profiles shot in 1963 and 1964 it was soon clear that there were considerable variations in interval velocities with depth, and that much data was required to determine velocity depth functions that would be adequate to convert the reflection sections into depth profiles.

Even in the 1960s it was realised that if all reflection horizons were conformable, erroneous velocity functions would have little effect on the structural picture. Isochron highs would still exist as highs when converted to depth; the actual depth to any point would be wrong but the general shape of the structure would still be valid and the choice of a drilling location would not depend on the velocity function used.

In the southern North Sea, horizons are not always conformable. Due to the diapiric nature of the Permian salt and the subsequent rapid lateral changes in thickness, depth and interval velocity of the overlying Mesozoic and Tertiary, closed isochron features on the base Zechstein cannot necessarily be assumed to exist as genuine closed structures.

Many wells were drilled during the 60s and 70s, but these were generally on or near the top of Mesozoic highs and so yield very limited data on the variation of interval velocity with depth. The bulk of velocity data had therefore to come from move-out studies or from development wells on basal Zechstein highs that are overlain by offset salt swells.

Early interpretations

The first isochron map (Fig. 5.21) of the basal Zechstein in the West Sole area was completed in July 1964 and showed a loosely defined high with a closure of at least 100 millisec. lying with a NNW axis across block 48/6. The block was applied for on the basis of this map.

After concession allocations in September 1964, four lines were shot within the block during October and November, 1964. All the 1962, 1963 and 1964 data were used in the construction of the isochron map which was considered reasonably reliable.

Conversion to depth presented a problem as no wells had been drilled at this time and most of the seismic data were too poor to yield reliable data from moveout analysis on the basal Zechstein reflection. The top and bottom of the salt however could be mapped with confidence, and various wells drilled though the Zechstein salt in Germany and Holland had shown a reasonably constant salt velocity of about 4,400 m/sec; the main problem therefore was the identification of the Mesozoic reflections (Tertiary being absent locally) and the selection of suitable velocity functions for the Mesozoic.

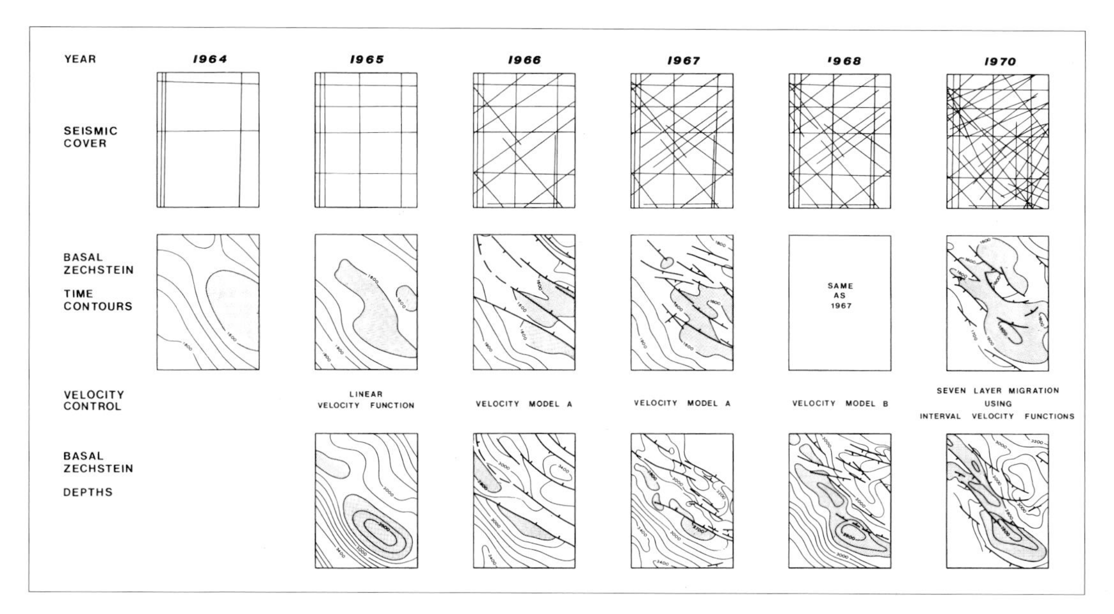

Fig. 5.21 Evolution of basal Zechstein structure map.

Corrections were applied to this velocity function for the effect of dip, but the feathering angle was not measured in these early surveys. This analysis yielded a surface-to-top Zechstein-salt velocity curve over a limited range of reflection times (1.1 to 1.4 sec) as reflection quality decayed beyond these limits.

Generally, over quite large depth ranges, interval velocity-depth curves approximate to straight lines. Since the surface-to-top-Permian curve was approximately linear over the observed time range, it was assumed that this straight line could be extrapolated in both directions. This velocity function was then used to convert reflection times to the top salt to depth. The top Zechstein salt is of little interest for its own sake. However its accurate delineation represents an essential stage in compiling a depth map on the base Zechstein. A constant salt velocity (4,400 m/sec) was used for the incremental interval to basal Zechstein. It was decided to test the base Zechstein structure at the highest point indicated on this interpretation and well 48/6-1 was spudded.

Velocity model

Following the discovery of commercial gas in December 1965, a detailed survey was shot over the structure in the summer of 1966. The general shape of the time high was similar to that of 1965 but faults which could not then be correlated because of insufficient coverage and poor quality data, were now mapped.

Mesozoic events still could not be followed with confidence so a velocity model was constructed using the 48/6-1 well data. This was developed by creating interval velocity v. depth functions for all the major stratigraphic units in the well using moveout data, and published data, and adjusting them to best fit the moveout data for the top Zechstein salt.

The model was extended up and down flank using the scanty seismic data available to control the thickness variations in the Mesozoic intervals. It was then assumed that these maintained a constant thickness in the Mesozoic strike direction. This enabled a velocity function from surface to top salt to be constructed and used even where the individual Mesozoic units could not be followed.

Again, a constant salt velocity was used. The resulting depth map had clearly reduced the crestal area of the main structure.

Additional detail shot towards the end of 1966 was incorporated into the 1967 interpretation. In the depth map we now see a third lobe developing in the north west corner of the block. In the earlier interpretations only two culminations appeared.

Stratigraphic data available

This interpretation used the same time map as the 1967 version but employed a more sophisticated velocity treatment. This was constructed as was Model A, but had access to stratigraphic data from the various wells on the West Sole field and from others in the vicinity. Functions were modified to give a best fit to the shapes of an extensive moveout velocity analysis (from surface to top Permian) by an iterative process.

Model B fitted the available well data to better than 2%. However, most wells lay in the southern portion of the field so it was important to estimate the validity of the model further north. The move-out data were split into two groups, north and south, to see whether there was a measurable difference in the velocity function along the salt axis. It was found that any variation was probably less than 3%.

From the first seven West Sole wells, and many others in the North Sea and onshore Holland, 4,400 m/sec. appears the best assumption for salt velocity, but the problem lies in defining the thickness and velocities of the various non-salt layers within the Zechstein column. Were these always present, and of constant velocity and thickness, their effects on base Zechstein depths could be easily calculated. Unfortunately, when the salt starts to flow the anhydrite is broken into a number of blocks or rafts, and some of these are carried by the salt flow, and often deformed beyond recognition. Generally BP could not define limits of these beds, and so a constant velocity had to be used until sufficient Zechstein data was available for a more elaborate treatment.

Locally we found that the Z3 anhydrite sometimes gave a very good reflection, and in the southwestern part of the 48/6 block it could be followed on all the lines.

Where the anhydrite exists in the unfractured state, the thickness is around 120 m and velocity about 6,000 m/sec. When it is fractured and carried away by the salt flow, it is replaced by salt with a velocity of 4,400 m/sec and this has the effect of apparently lowering the base Zechstein depth profile by 32 m (just over 1%). Over most of the area we cannot say whether the Z3 is present in the salt column or not.

The depth map resulting from this more elaborate velocity treatment looks markedly different, especially in the vicinity of well 48/6-10 and 18, from the 1967 interpretation of the same time data.

Final interpretation

The late-1969 surveys were designed to seek possible extensions to the productive area of the West Sole field. By this time 21 wells had been drilled of which 19 were producers. With the improved quality of the 1969 data it was possible to follow several Mesozoic horizons over the entire field area.

Interval velocity function

Interval functions were built up using the same general approach as for models A and B, but there were now 21 wells available over the feature, and although they were generally on the Crestal area in the Basal Zechstein they straddled quite a wide range of depths through Mesozoic intervals. It was still necessary, however to extrapolate the function beyond the limits of well control and the simple straight line approach gives in many cases ridiculously low velocities at shallow depths and improbably high velocities at large depths.

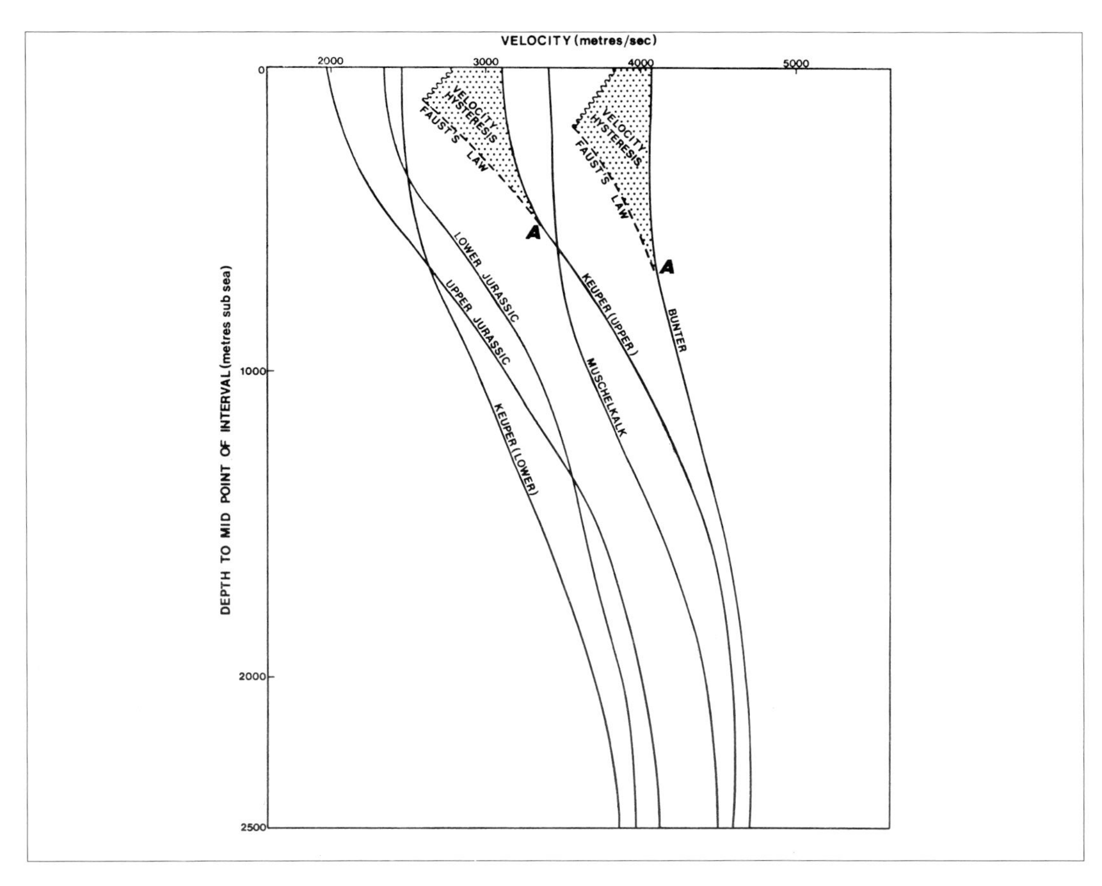

Fig. 5.22
Interval velocity functions, 1970.

If the change of interval velocity with depth is due only to the increased compaction due to the greater weight of overburden then Gassman (1951) and Faust (1953) have both produced laws that allow a gradual increase in velocity with depth of burial. When we have subsequent uplift of a deeply buried interval, however, we would not generally expect that its interval velocity will decrease to fit these simple laws. This would assume perfect elasticity over very long periods of time, and ignores any effects of in situ cementation.

So, we might expect the interval velocity for, say, the Bunter Sandstones or Upper Keuper over the top of a salt swell, to be controlled more by the greatest depth of burial during its geological history than by its present depth. The Faust or Gassman curve probably still applies for intervals now lying at their historically greatest depth but must be modified as suggested in Fig. 5.22 for intervals subsequently uplifted. The choice of starting point for this modification is complicated by continuing depression and deposition regionally in addition to the localized salt uplift. The extent of the velocity relaxation, or 'hysteresis' above point A (on the Upper Keuper curve of Fig. 5.22) depends on the lithology, extent of cementation and time scale of the movement. If well data fail to give control over the shape above A it is probably better to assume a constant or slightly decreasing velocity at shallow depth than the values given by either a straight line extrapolation or Faust or Gassman laws.

It is clear, therefore, that this velocity 'hysteresis' effect will be influenced by the entire burial history of the interval. Since the well velocity data we have available only cover the middle range of the curve, and we wish to study the Base Zechstein structure beneath the salt swell, where all the intervals are much shallower, an attempt had to be made to extrapolate the functions through this 'hysteresis' zone.

A study of the well data suggests that salt flow was initiated in the Upper Bunter, but was of small vertical extent at this stage (20-30 metres). As the entire area progressively depressed, and the weight of sediment increased, the velocity of salt movements also increased, so that 100 metres or so of movement had taken place by the end of the Keuper. The bulk of the movement took place during the Jurassic (2000 metres).

The velocity functions used in the depth conversion attempted to use this history of estimating 'hysteresis' effect on the velocity curves. The functions actually used for depth conversion and migration are indicated on Fig. 5.22, each function being approximated to three straight lines for presentation to the computer. Although we believe these functions accurately define the velocities over the West sole field, they clearly should not be used over other features in the area, as apart from regional variations in the individual lithologies, which affect the entire velocity curve, the 'hysteresis' effect will be different over each Salt uplift.

By 1973 seven horizons were mapped and these are shown on the seismic section in Fig. 5.23. The main purpose in interpreting these horizons was to obtain more

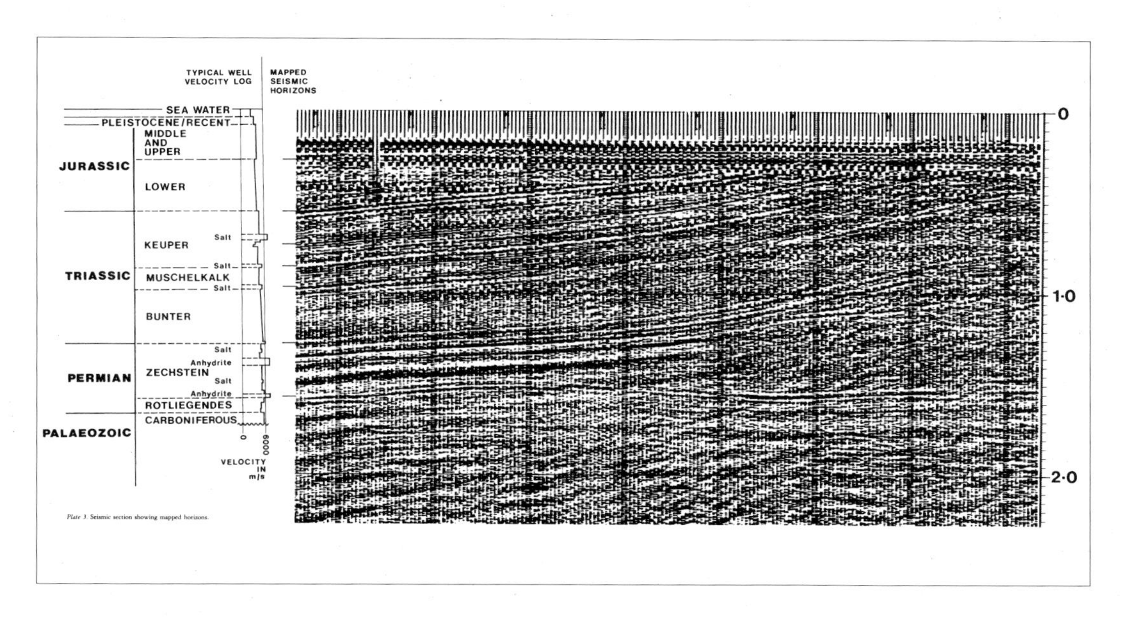

Fig. 5.23
Seismic section showing mapped horizons.

accurate depth conversion to the basal Zechstein. By using individual interval velocities, allowance could be made for outcropping beds and varying formation thickness. The time map produced shows the same general high area as previously, but it is further complicated by additional faults.

To convert to depth and account for migrated travel paths a full migration was performed using all seven intervals mapped. Isochron maps were drawn of these horizons and synthetic time values prepared for migration along chosen lines. In this manner, an attempt to treat a three dimensional migration has been made using only two dimensions.

Final maps

The further we stray from well control, the more uncertain our velocity functions become, but BP believed by 1973 that within the field the velocity function used was in error by no more than 2%.

By 1974 BP was in little doubt that many of the early exploration holes in the Rotliegend gas area were drilled on apparent, but not real structures, and that several genuine structures were so destroyed by velocity effects that they had yet to be recognised".

3. **The British Contribution**

Nigel Anstey offers this personal view:

"Historically, as noted earlier, oil exploration has been an American skill. No one would wish to detract from the American achievement. In geophysics particularly, the

vast majority of the technical advances that have made modern seismics so effective originated in the States. It was the Geophysical Analysis Group at MIT that gave birth to the digital revolution, and it was oil companies like Esso and Mobil and Amoco that nurtured it. Among the contractors, GSI contributed many major advances; GSI had been the first, and it kept its lead for many years. As the North Sea excitement developed, it was Norman Hempstead who had the briefcase most stuffed with goodies.

The combination of the digital revolution and the North Sea led many international contractors to set up in Britain; before long the established list of SSL, GSI and Western was supplemented by Petty Ray, Seiscom, Prakla-Seismos, CGG, Digicon, Sefel, Rogers, GECO, and the only home-grown British company Horizon. In general, however, the international companies treated their British offices as bases for marketing, processing and recruitment; all research and development remained back home.

Because of this, the story of creative petroleum geophysics in Britain lies largely with just three companies: BP and SSL, later joined by Seiscom. (The contribution of British universities to real-life petroleum geophysics was a long long time in coming.)

BP had maintained a research effort for many years, in the team of Dennison and Wood (who wrote the definitive paper on geophone design, and made significant contributions to the synthetic seismogram). Later O'Brien intensified the work on synthetics, and was later supported by Hosken and Walden and Lucas and White. Their work lies behind every successful well tie made today. Meanwhile Al-Chalabi was doing his classic work on velocities, and Hornabrook his on depth conversion; to many of us at the time, this was our baptism into the fire of depth conversion.

Likewise SSL had maintained a development effort for many years. When SSL was set up in 1947 there was no foreign exchange to buy American equipment; the Brits had to learn how to make all the amplifiers and geophones, and the rest of it, at home. Over the years the development effort widened, and the first ship to work in the North Sea (after Shell's famous flying boat) was equipped almost exclusively with instruments and gear of British manufacture. Nobody remembers that ship kindly (the SS Seislim could roll on a wet blanket), but it did discover many of the early North Sea fields.

So we should take a moment to remember the names of the men who did the creative work: of Baird, and Lerwill, and Kennett, and Newman, and Cane, and Castleberg, and Breugelmans, and Hawkins. The equipment they designed has long since rusted away, but they remain the unsung heros of British geophysics - the fellows who put it all together, and made it work, and got it there on time.

SSL also performed a sterling service to Britain in training so many of the geophysicists who developed the North Sea. Perhaps this was merely because SSL did not pay very well, and so had a high turnover on its field crews. But at one time a meeting of oil- company chief geophysicists in London would have looked like a meeting of the ex-SSL club.

SSL - under the benign governance of van der Linden and Fitch - also had the insight to maintain a modest effort in research. Before the North Sea, this effort had already produced the first device capable of producing a corrected cross-section in the field, the first implementation of a spherical-spreading correction, the median filter, the magnetic correlator that first made the Vibroseis system practical, the concept of short-period multiples and the stratigraphic filter, and an independent device for attenuating marine reverberations at both the source and the receiver.

In the early years of the North Sea, it supplemented this last device with a real-time Hall-effect correlator that took the guesswork out of sea-floor reverberation times and reflection coefficients. The combination of the two devices vastly improved our ability to see beneath the salt in the southern North Sea.

Later, the effort yielded the now-standard techniques for offshore check-shooting (and VSP), the feedback method for the attenuation of long-period surface multiples, Newman's famous Pinch of Salt, and a wondrous machine to migrate sections (later totally eclipsed, it must be said, by the simple and elegant diffraction stack devised by Rockwell of GSI).

When Seiscom set up in Britain in 1969, its primary function was to offer the impressive processing advances pioneered in the States by Taner - the first man to beat GSI on their home ground.

(Modesty has caused Nigel to exclude his own name from the innovations listed in the last couple of pages, but his contribution to the developments mentioned, early on with SSL, later with Seiscom, was probably second to none - ed.)

However, it did produce two British developments. One of these was the modern spec survey. Some group-shoot and speculative work had been done earlier in the States; the novelty now was the concept of searching out new basins, designing surveys specifically for them, doing the acquisition and processing, and preparing an interpretation and report. Initially there was considerable hostility to this concept. However, many of the plays that later emerged in the northern North Sea, the Celtic Sea, Cardigan Bay, the Porcupine Basin, the Irish Sea and (still of topical interest) West of Shetlands were derived from Seiscom spec surveys shot in the early 1970s.

The other British development at Seiscom, in 1971, was the display of seismic attributes in colour. To a young geophysicist today, seated at her workstation, colour must seem obvious, and a world without colour inconceivable. But everything that is standard practice today was once just an idea - advanced enthusiastically by the converted, and derided by the rest.

There could not be a better example than colour. To the converted, it was a way of increasing the dynamic range, and of conveying that increased information to the eye instantly. To the rest, it was just a pretty gimmick. The memory is still vivid of a trip to the Hague, to show Shell some early examples from the northern North Sea. They were in no doubt at all: it was rubbish, of no technical value at all. (To be fair, they have changed their minds since.)

Two mysteries persist from those early days of colour. One was a rebuff from Schlumberger, who did not feel that the display of well logs needed any help at all - either to aid visual correlation or to enhance dynamic range. That still seems a strange judgement.

The other was a rebuff from the radiologists. Even in 1971, one could take an ordinary photographic x-ray, scan it digitally, contour the density in colour (with adjacent contour intervals in contrasting colours), and the x-ray would spring into new life. Not only was the bone/tissue distinction enhanced, but the most subtle variations of tissue density became visually obvious. However, they said no. Ah well, we thought, by the time our lives become dependent on an x-ray diagnosis the radiologists will have changed their minds; by then everything will be digital, and in colour. Somebody should get a move on.

So this is one personal view of the seismic scene in the early years of the PESGB. For us who lived through those years, it was a time we shall never forget.

Not that it wasn't wearing. We had more excitement than we needed, and sometimes we longed to be free of it. We longed for stability, and order, and time to take the kids to the beach. But it was the time of our lives, the time when we made a difference.

Or was it just that we were young?"

Chapter Six

The First Oilfields (Pre Fourth Round)

1969 was the year things really started to happen. Many explorers, unbeknown to themselves, were soon about to reap the rewards from their earlier efforts and technical advances. Some explorers were fortunate enough to make their first introductions into the North Sea at this time. Myles Bowen remembers:

"As geologist working for Shell I had the advantage of having spent 15 years working overseas before I was recalled from South America in the spring of 1969 to participate in the early days of North Sea exploration. Taking over as exploration manager in London was not at that time considered to be a particularly promising assignment; if it had been, I doubt if I would have been offered the job! You may wonder why I say 'not promising'; well the current view then, not only in Shell, was that all the worthwhile gas fields in the southern North Sea had already been found, while the search for oil in the north was doomed to failure! When I arrived on the scene in May 1969 nine wells had been drilled in the northern part of the U.K. sector without making a single commercial discovery. Shell was the only company then drilling in UK northern waters and apart from fulfilling its work obligations, had no further programme there. Shell's London management under George Williams certainly were confident that oil would be found, but were unable to secure additional budget funds for 1970 on a 'no-success' basis".

Indeed, Sir Eric Drake, Chairman of BP (quoted in Clive Callow, "Power from the sea search for North Sea Oil and Gas" [Gollancz1973]) said of the North Sea as late as April 1970. "There won't be a major field there". Others have volunteered to drink every drop of oil found there! However, such negative speculations were soon to terminally cease. Leslie Illing describes how interest in potential oil deposits in the north began to gain momentum:

"Up to this point discoveries had followed a pattern in keeping with the geological speculation based on the initial discoveries. The distribution of the various facies belts of the Lower Permian sands and red-beds were established, and the limits of the sedimentary basins were outlined. The significance of the Mid-North-Sea-High, limiting the basin to the north, and its link with the Market Weighton axis (already well established in British geological literature) became clear.

Speculation began about what lay further north. It is easy now to point to the several grabens (Viking, Central, etc) that bisect the North Sea, and to ascribe them to incipient rifting associated with the opening of the Atlantic. These phenomena have become common parlance in the last 30 years. But at the time we are considering, such hypotheses were far less widely accepted. Geologists pointed to the Lower Palaeozoic fold belt of NW Scotland and Norway, and, inspite of the offset, assumed it was continuous in between. Such now seems a most unwarranted assumption; but this was not so 30 years ago.

Indeed it was with wonder and excitement that geologists in the exploration industry viewed the first seismic lines across the Viking Graben. There displayed before those privileged to behold them was clear evidence of significant Tertiary basins, to be confirmed by the later discovery of Palaeocene oil fields."

Myles Bowen takes up the story:

"To start off, all we knew from geophysics was that there was a 10,000 ft deep Tertiary basin flanked by shallow basement or Palaeozoic rocks, but with indications of thick underlying Mesozoic sequences, at least in the central, deeper parts. Prior to drilling there was no reported evidence of the presence of hydrocarbons, although if anyone had bothered to consult the North Sea fishermen they might have discovered otherwise!

The first potential reservoirs defined were sands of Palaeocene age near the base of the Tertiary section, although these were not ubiquitous. Once the presence of oil had been established, controversy raged until the mid-seventies as to its source. Shell geologists were reasonably certain that it came from the Kimmeridge, as not only had they typed it, but they knew that its most commonly promoted rival, shale of Palaeocene age, was both relatively lean and immature, i.e. not deeply enough buried. I doubt whether this specific advantage that Shell had over the competition actually gained that company any extra hydrocarbons, at least in the northern North Sea. There the initial exploration activity consisted of looking for structures of whatever age or composition as defined by seismic and drilling them; there was little scope for such a sophisticated approach.

Consortia drilled the best looking structural prospects they had managed to secure in order of preference. It was not always the best that brought success; the Ekofisk discovery, the first giant oilfield to be discovered was the sixth and, I have been told, final well on Phillips's programme in Norway. It was a complete surprise to most people (perhaps to Phillips too) as it was clearly a discovery in the Chalk. If there was one thing we all knew for certain it was that the Chalk was not an oil reservoir, at least, not one to produce at the prolific rates Phillips quoted. Ekofisk originally contained 2.3 bn recoverable barrels of oil, not to mention over 5 tcf of gas.

I suppose, in a way, Ekofisk should have warned us that we were in for many surprises in the Northern North Sea. We puzzled over the seismic; to some it looked like a reef, others even suggested that it was a buried volcano! The real reason for the peculiar shape seen on seismic time sections at the Chalk level is the effect of the anomalous velocity of the overlying sediments; many structures, like Ekofisk, have a so-called 'gas chimney' above them, a column of very low velocity gas impregnated sediment. Many of us in the early days mistook these features for salt or clay diapirs."

Peter Walmsley continues, recalling BP's involvement at this time particularly citing the fact that it was a BP rig, on contract to Amoco, that drilled the UK's first commercial discovery:

"Turning back to the North Sea I must mention the start of North Sea oil, as distinct from Southern North Sea gas. Blocks encompassing the Forties Field were applied for in late 1965, before the discovery of gas in the south. Quite large tracts of acreage between 50° and 58° latitude were awarded in the Second Round to a handful of companies, Shell/Esso having the lion's share. Applications and drilling commitments made at this time were very much an act of faith or a shot in the dark, whichever way you wish to look at it. There were no rigs capable of drilling in those water depths at the time, whilst if finds were made it was not known how they might be produced nor how pipelines might be laid in such water depths.

It is worth recalling the data available at the time of those applications. It was pretty basic. The nearest well was Amoseas 38/29-1. Broad reconnaissance seismic surveys shot in 1962 and 1964 were of poor quality and almost featureless. The very few reflectors indicated what was probably a simple Tertiary basin reaching a depth of about 12,000ft. There was no obvious deeper data. A very slight turnover west of Block 21/9 mapped out as a gentle nose extending eastwards into the basin. No closure was mapped. It was on this basis that BP applied for and were awarded Blocks 21/9 and 21/10.

Fig. 6.1
The 'Sea Quest' under tow in 1966).

By 1970 several things had happened to make the prospects look distinctly more promising. A number of wells had been drilled in northern waters. Shell/Esso in particular had carried out a significant drilling programme using their Staflo rig, albeit with not terribly encouraging results. BP's Sea Quest (see Fig. 6.1) actually drilled its first northern well under contract to Amoco. This well, 22/18-1, was the Montrose discovery made in December 1969 at almost the same time as Phillips discovered Ekofisk in Norwegian waters. This was the first British offshore oil find. Amoco were desperate to keep their information secret, but I cannot say that they were very successful as far as BP were concerned. Never contract a competitor's rig to drill a critical exploration well!"

Myles Bowen adds:

"Montrose was a large, but very low relief structure where again uppermost Palaeocene sands formed the reservoir. In fact, there were two adjacent structures with the discovery well located on the part now known as Arbroath. Reserves in these two accumulations originally amounted to 210 mbbl."

This discovery had already wetted the appetites of an oil-hungry industry, and it was not long before the big one followed. Peter Walmsley gives this account:

"By 1970, BP had mapped a very large top Palaeocene closure within its Blocks 21/9 and 21/10. Previously Gulf/Shell had jointly drilled 22/6-1 on a small culmination separated from the main BP structure by a low saddle. We had acquired the data from this well by exchange and the information excited us greatly. 22/6-1 contained some ratty oil-bearing sands overlying a very thick water-bearing sandstone. The closure over Blocks 21/9 and 21/10 was such as to carry that clean sandstone several hundreds of feet above the oil-water contact in the ratty sands. Could it be possibly be.......

Armed with this information the general management of a rather impoverished BP (Prudhoe Bay had not been found then) were persuaded not to farm the blocks out as they had been contemplating but rather to drill without delay. I do not believe that George Williams of Shell ever realised how close he was to pulling off a coup of stupendous proportions!

In the late 1960's BP had moved its operations base from Eakring to the old police station at Great Yarmouth. At least the records were secure in their prison cell! The Sea Quest was run from a small forward office in Bridge Street, Aberdeen. In the autumn of 1970 the rig moved to drill 21/10-1.

It was soon clear that this well exceeded all our expectations. The sands were clean to the top of the Palaeocene, the oil-water contact was the same as in 22/6-1, recoverable reserves of at least 1.8 billion barrels were proven and, above all, the well came in within about 3ft of prediction.

Fig. 6.2 Production platform FA (Graythorp - 1) in BP's Forties oilfield.

At the time security of information was paramount. All drilling and geological messages were scrambled or transmitted in code - except one. We had stopped to core a few feet above the reservoir and this first core was pulled, inevitably, in the small hours of the morning. I was by then the regional geologist and Laurie Horobin was our senior geologist in Great Yarmouth. Knowing I was anxious to hear the result he threw caution to the wind and phoned me at home at about 4am. I will always remember his guarded words: just three words which amply described the North Sea story to this day. 'Peter', he said 'it looks good'. 'That's fine', I said, 'thanks for calling', and contentedly went back to sleep.

Thus was the momentous news conveyed. It was October 1970. North Sea oil was well and truly on the way".

This, of course, was the Forties field - the second giant oil field to be discovered in the North Sea, and the first in British waters. Myles Bowen continues the story:

"Already two plays had been proven and a third followed shortly afterwards.Shell had obtained block 30/16 in the 3rd Round in 1970 which contained a large structurally high horst adjacent to the deep Tertiary basin. It was predicted that a good Rotliegend sand reservoir might be sourced by mature Kimmeridge shales which abutted it on two sides. The objective was a giant field, but the cored Rotliegend sands turned out to contain only dead oil shows. Unexpectedly a thin Zechstein carbonate section was also present, but this had not been cored. A decision had to be made whether or not to test the Zechstein which had live oil shows while drilling. Shell drilling engineers were never keen to carry out DST's (drill stem tests) on floating rigs and it was not until slices of vuggy dolomite bleeding live oil had been recovered using Schlumberger's Tricore sidewall slicer that a decision to test was taken.

To everyone's amazement the well tested at prolific rates and Shell's Auk field had been found. This third play-type was rapidly followed by the similar Argyll discovery by Hamilton."

Fig. 6.3 *'Opening the tap' of the first offshore oil brought ashore - from the Argyll Field described below.*

David Warwick describes the discovery of the Argyll Field as follows - an account which pays particular credit to the skills of a good wellsite geologist:

"The Argyll Field was discovered by Hamilton Brothers. The first exploration well on block 30/24 was drilled on a Palaeocene high and like many other wells at the time was targeting the Palaeocene sands. The Pre-Cretaceous was poorly imaged on seismic and poorly understood north of the Mid-North Sea High. 30/24-1 was drilled in 1969 through the Palaeocene (no sand) and on through the Chalk and reached T.D in the Permian Zechstein. The well was logged and then plugged and abandoned dry. Subsequently, Hamilton used the services of a consultant wellsite geologist from Exploration Logging to prepare the Well Report and composite log for the 30/24-1. The geologist in question, Howard Dewhirst, requested a set of dried cuttings to be able to check lithologies in preparing the composite log descriptions. When he got to the Zechstein sequence he observed vuggy porosity in the dolomite, live oil fluorescence under the UV light box, and when he put the cuttings in the blender, also registered a gas show. Howard duly informed Hamilton's Exploration Manager that he believed that the first well had intersected a potential oil reservoir, and that was how the 30/24-2 well in 1971 came to be drilled at a location close to the No.1 well and how the Argyll field was discovered."

It is left to Myles Bowen and Roderick Archer to conclude this section on the earliest (but in many ways the most dramatic) discoveries made on acreage awarded during the first three UK licensing rounds. The fourth licensing round was announced 22 June 1971, but while that event in itself was startling, its impact could have been seriously eclipsed by the discovery of the giant Brent Field at about the same time (July). Maybe that was one reason the discovery was kept quiet until after the awards. Myles Bowen begins:

"Despite the fact that two giant fields had been discovered and that at least three plays already existed, enthusiasm in the industry for the area was slow to take hold, as drilling figures for these northern areas up to 1971 demonstrate. It must be admitted however that not too many rigs capable of drilling in such a hostile environment were available. Another restricting factor throughout the early years of exploration was the inability of the early rigs to cope with the abnormally high pressures encountered, particularly in over-pressured shaley sequences below the Chalk. A stack with blowout preventers capable of withstanding even 10,000 psi was a rarity at that time.

Six weeks before the 4th Round was sprung on the industry Shell moved its small Staflo semi-submersible rig up to 61° North to test a large prospect, close to the median line, which it had acquired in the 3rd Round of 1970. This was some 150 miles north of the most northerly well previously drilled in the North Sea and was in fact the northernmost offshore well in the world at that time. The Viking Graben had already been defined by seismic. It ran from the Central Graben, closely following the median line. North of 60° however it widened or developed a shallower flanking area now known as the East Shetland Basin. The prospect to be drilled flanked the graben proper on the eastern edge of the East Shetland Basin and was a large tilted fault block containing bedded sediments lying below a substantial unconformity around the base of the Cretaceous. The fault block to be tested was one of many, most of which dipped westwards, away from the Viking Graben.

The difficulty was to prognose the age and prospectivity of the underlying pre - Cretaceous sediments, which were expected to be the main objective. Our prognosis was for Jurassic over Triassic sediments, although some thought the rocks might be of Palaeozoic, or even pre-Cambrian age. The basis for this prognosis was that on reassembling the continents into their Mesozoic position we saw that the East Shetland basin occupied an analogous position to the Scoresbysund area of East Greenland and indeed was then almost as close to it as to the Jurassic outcrops of the UK. Recently published geological cross-sections of the Wollaston foreland in East Greenland so closely resembled the pre-Cretaceous relief we saw on the seismic profiles that we became reasonably convinced of our prognosis; this of course turned out to be correct. I tell this story in some detail as at a talk on Brent given by a Shell speaker in the mid 80's, the giant Brent field with 2.0 bn bbl oil and 4 tcf gas which resulted from that well was referred to as an 'accidental' discovery!"

Roderick Archer gives his account:

"I was lucky enough to spend the 1970's as an assistant with Shell Expro. in London. My first supervisor was an American geologist - in fact, in those days there were many Americans in the Company in London teaching us how to do it (find and produce oil that is). It was a happy atmosphere, you got to know everyone and there was plenty of the learning process. There were no computers as far as I recall except the mainframe computers that relied heavily on card input.

After literally only a short time there in London working in the Viking Graben I had limited exposure to the famous sealed bids in the Fourth Round of UKCS licensing. After the auction, which I watched on the TV news, I realised that it would not be too long before the boys in Aberdeen mobilised one of their rigs (possibly Staflo) onto a new location way up north in the Viking Graben. My supervisor in my office was responsible for scouting. His job was to phone round the industry each Monday to ask for an update of competitors' drilling activities. In return he had to divulge what Shell was up to. 'Oh, we have moved that rig to block two-one-one or two eleven, if you prefer, and here are the provisional co-ordinates ...'. I remember this man telling me how the industry scouts found it hard to believe that we had actually gone on to the location: 'Up there?? What's up there??' (Little did they know, and now it is all oil and gas history.) No doubt Her Majesty's Treasury was thankful that this venture was so successful - What would they have done without it?

A young geologist who had just joined us from Texaco was running round in a bit of a flap. The third round well 211/29-1 was about to land a core and there were doubts whether senior staff from London would be allowed to witness a find. I believe the Exploration Manager of the day was allowed onto the drill floor, but only after a lot of security checking (in fact part of my exploration floor in London was virtually sealed off during the crucial days of interpretation). We were watched like hawks. But we had found the famous Brent field and that is what mattered.

Some years later, when I was a successful wellsite geologist, I was present in the Toolpushers office witnessing a curious conversation. The well had been a good one, masses of core had been cut and here was yet another find. A helicopter had landed and in walked two engineers. They introduced themselves to the Dutch toolpusher as being from Expro; they were here for testing. 'Yes, I know, but what is your name? Who are you? Where are you from?' questioned the Toolpusher. Again the two Englishmen emphasised that they were from Expro. 'I know that', said the unhappy Dutchman, 'I too am with Expro, but I want to know who you are?'

The two men from Reading looked at each other. 'Well. we're from Expro....Look' and the two men took out their cards and showed the poor unhappy and confused Dutchman their Company logo. 'Ah, so' said the Dutchman in a loud voice, 'You have moved to Reading - that is good, I am sure.' The two Englishmen pointed out that it was Expro come to help Expro, as per the contract. There were no more questions. Just puzzled look. At least they were all working together."

Fig. 6.4
'A matter of scale'. Artists impression of 'SEDCO-K' drilling platform superimposed on Trafalgar Square, London - 1971.

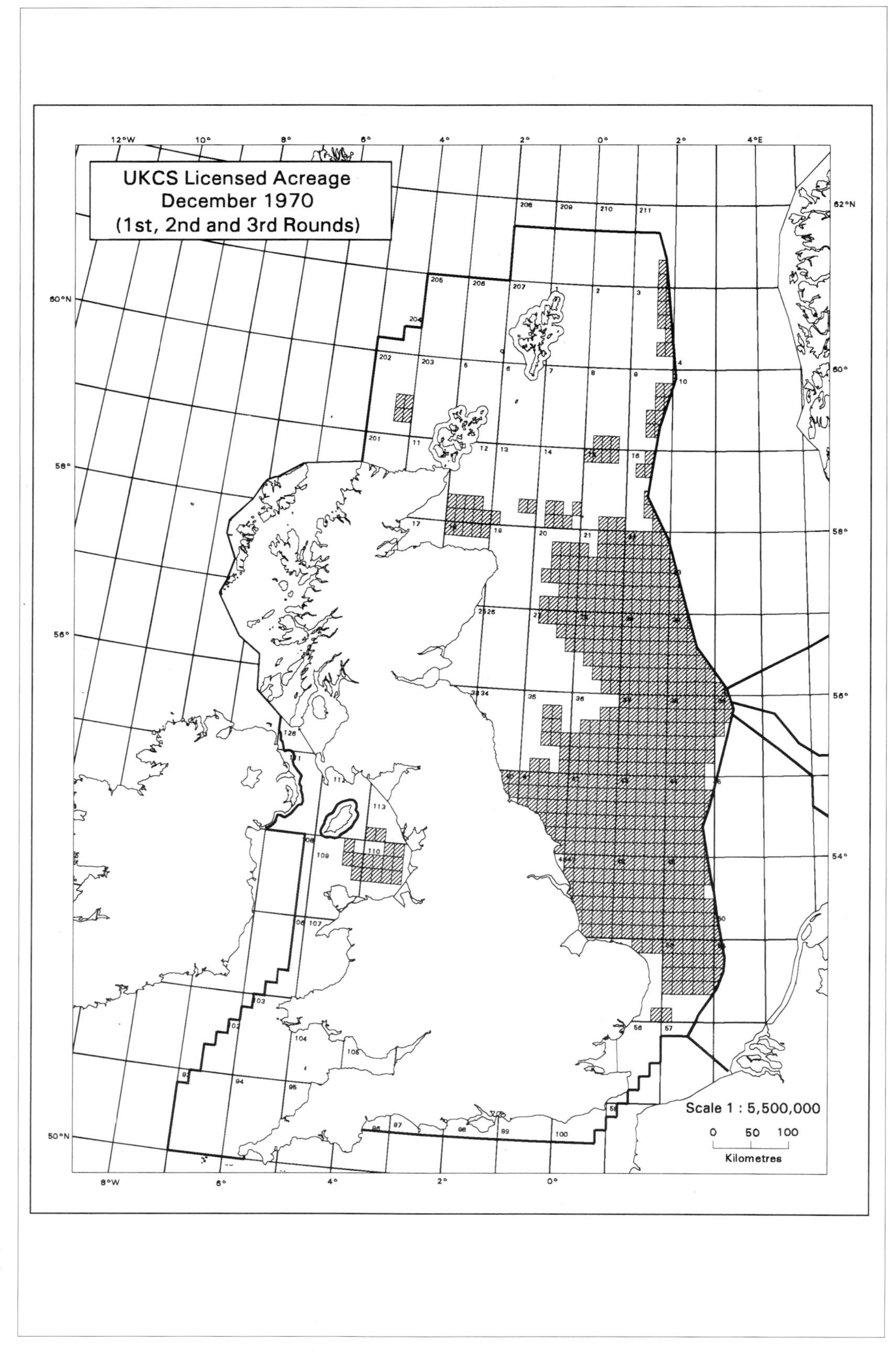

Fig.6.5
UKCS licensed acreage - pre 4th Round in December 1970.

Chapter Seven

Discoveries Flourish - and Tales of Drilling

1. North Sea : Fourth Round and Beyond

The Fourth Round hit the UK oil industry like a bull in a china shop. The broken china in this example, probably belonged to Edward Heath's Conservative Government who were accused from all sides of essentially giving away the North Sea with highly generous fiscal terms and no state participation - the antithesis of nationalisation. The impending energy crisis weakened the government even further, while the oil companies ('the bulls' if you like) were free to rage onwards and upwards. Profits soared.

For those around at the time, this was an extraordinary development - particularly the 'sealed bid' policy for 15 designated blocks. Myles Bowen recalls:

"In 1971 someone at the Department of Energy, or its Secretary of State suffered a brainstorm and put on offer on 22nd June, 278 of the remaining blocks in the North Sea, (as well as 158 blocks in other offshore areas) including 15 blocks for cash bids - an unheard-of development. It was just what was needed to bring the North Sea to the attention of the worldwide oil industry; only 60 days were allowed to decide which blocks to bid for and how much to offer.

Shell had plugged and abandoned their discovery as an untested 'tight hole'. Many blocks were now on offer in the area still referred to as the Brent Province. We knew we had discovered another giant field, and from analysis of the seismic it looked as if there were many more fields to be found in the Viking Graben proper and the East Shetland Basin. The tilted fault blocks formed closed highs or ridges at the easily mapped Base Cretaceous level. Within some of the fault blocks internal reflections could be clearly seen, whereas in others they were difficult or impossible to discern. Here we made a mistake. In Brent these reflectors were associated mainly with the Middle to Lower Jurassic sandstones; the more thinly bedded Trias gave rise to few reflections. Some of the larger 'bumps' at base Cretaceous had few coherent reflectors below them; these we deduced might have Triassic rocks subcropping the Cretaceous and consequently would have less reservoir potential. Two of such highs, thus categorized, turned out to be the Ninian and Beryl fields, the largest in the UK sector after Brent; Jurassic sands were in fact present in both!

One block which had clear internal reflectors was 211/21 which was one of the only two blocks offered for cash north of 60°. It contained a large structure extending south into block 211/26. Given a Brent type reservoir and the size of the structure another giant field seemed a possibility. Shell and Esso were determined to cash in on their competitive advantage and make sure of securing at least this attractive block in the auction. The estimated value of the block on a risked basis was not far off £100m; the question was: how much to bid to be sure of getting it. There was always uncertainty as to the 'tightness' of the Brent discovery, particularly as the well had 'kicked' slightly with oil to surface, a fact well known to the entire crew of the rig.

The partners differed widely on the price required to secure the block and the sum finally bid was a compromise. Bids were to be delivered to the Department of Energy by noon on 20th August 1971 and were opened in public the same afternoon. It was a spectacular occasion attended by many of the notables in the oil world. Bid envelopes were opened and the bids read out in order of quadrant number. The first few bids to be announced were for a few hundred thousand pounds or less and created little surprise. Then the envelope containing the Shell/Esso bid was produced; the first bid read out was £4m for block 9/13 (now Beryl). This substantial bid created a considerable stir among the audience. Two minor bids followed and finally Angus Beckett, the Under Secretary, read out 'block 211/21, 21 million' and the remainder of the bid was drowned in general confusion that ensued and which took several minutes to subside. It was an exciting occasion, never, sadly, to be repeated, since in subsequent rounds cash bids have been opened by DoE officials in private".

So, following the Fourth Round results, exploration flourished and new plays continued to be found - some, perhaps, by luck - others by genuine exploration initiative. Drilling boomed and, in those early seventies, a number of our contributors had particular memories of events offshore - not all of them particularly conducive to good health and safety records! Bruce Blanche recalls an airborne incident (in November 1973) while he was working on one of the first new semi-submersibles in block 211/28 on the Hutton Field:

"In those days, there was no such thing as a set period offshore. One merely went offshore until told to come back to the office. Conoco had their operating base at Dundee, and so one normally flew from Dundee Riverside Airport, which was then a grass airstrip running parallel to the Tay, with the famous railway bridge at its eastern end, which always made for an interesting takeoff. Departures were always early morning and the passengers suitably bleary eyed after a night of carousing. The flight to Aberdeen to catch the fixed-wing aircraft to Sumburgh took 30 minutes in a light aircraft. The aircraft to Sumburgh was an aged DC-3 (Dakota) which had seen wartime service, was already a veteran and should have been in a warbird museum. These DC- 3s were operated by Air Anglia, the precursor of Air UK (see Fig. 7.1). They were fairly basic inside and noisy, with a no-nonsense stewardess of mature years who could handle the most obnoxious oil worker. From Sumburgh the final leg to the rig was by Sikorsky S-61N, operated by Bristow Helicopters.

We were on one of the return trips from Sumburgh to Dyce on 20 November 1973, on the DC-3 affectionately known as Juliet Victor after the last two letters of its registration (G-AGJV). At the time this aircraft had been 31 years in service and was reportedly the oldest passenger-carrying aircraft in Western Europe. The Captain, Bain Porterfield, reported a suspected hydraulic leak. The passengers, happily ignorant of any problem, were rejoicing in their return to 'loved' ones from Sedco

702. My particular 'loved one' was heavily pregnant at the time. Looking out of the window I noticed a light aircraft flying alongside. In blissful ignorance I thought that maybe they were taking pictures. Meanwhile, Aberdeen Airport (Dyce) was on full alert, with emergency procedures in place. The landing wheels, stuck in the Semi-retracted position, were cranked down by hand by distraught co-pilot Roy Mann and, despite non-functioning flaps during a 30 minute circling session, a landing was attempted.

Fig. 7.1
Air Anglia .... your journey awaits!

The aircraft landed, profusely leaking hydraulic fluid, and the passengers were amazed at the number of emergency vehicles awaiting them, some even thinking the procedure was normal! This was an exciting end to a stint offshore with its own inherent dangers, which luckily for all ended happily. The aircraft went on to become a freight aircraft for Air Anglia and was then sold to Ethiopia".

Also in November 1973 (obviously a bad month!) David Warwick recalls a particularly severe storm in the central North Sea:

"The storm hit on the 19th November 1973 and caused considerable mayhem across the Central North Sea in particular (see Fig. 7.2). I was working for Hamilton Brothers at the time, doing wellsite duty on an Argyll field appraisal well.

Fig. 7.2
Storm on the 'Bluewater III'.

The rig drilling well 30/24-5 was the Bluewater III, one of the smallest semis ever to work in the North Sea. The storm hit as they were tripping out of the hole, so as luck would have it we had about 8,500ft of pipe in the derrick, which did not improve the stability of the semi! The wind built up to a steady 90mph, gusting up to 120mph, and one by one the rig's anchors popped apart until we ended up with just two anchors on one corner holding the rig in position. Each time the anchors broke, the rig swung around to a different heading and the balance shifted dramatically. At one point, the deck was tilting at 15 degrees which we later found out was just a few degrees off the critical angle at which the rig would have turned over. As the seas built up to around 70ft the last two anchors began to drag and we started to drift to the southeast, on a heading towards Rotterdam, according to the Superintendent. Mayday messages were duly transmitted and two ocean-going tugs were dispatched, one from Aberdeen and one from Hull. The skipper of the Aberdeen tug fell on the bridge on the way out and broke a leg, so the tug had to return to port. The other tug 'Euroman' from Hull (an Iceland Cod War veteran) caught up with the Bluewater III and eventually got a line attached. I was happy to be identified as one of the non-essential personnel to be evacuated by chopper several hours later. Apart from the skipper of the Aberdeen tug, no one else suffered any injuries".

Sometimes the conflicts were not so much 'man versus the elements 'but' man versus man'. Bruce Blanche recalls one particular culinary difference of opinion between Brits and Texans, referring fondly to 'The leg of lamb that swam':

"The jack-up Britannia, operated by Sante Fe based in Yarmouth, was drilling well 49/17-8 during late '72 and early '73 in the Southern Gas Basin. Britannia in those days boasted a host of characters, colourful in themselves. In those early days, the senior drillers and toolpushers were Americans from either Texas or Oklahoma, who had been used to working in the Gulf of Mexico and Nigeria and had very set views regarding 'good food'. In other words, if it wasn't steak or beef, it was only suitable for the natives.

On one occasion during my stint offshore, the supply boat from Yarmouth had offloaded catering supplies which included legs of lamb. As most of the roughnecks were either Scots or from the North of England, they naturally looked forward to a good Sunday roast with all the trimmings. When the Texan toolpushers casually asked 'Cookie' 'what you'all got for chow today?', Cookie replied in his Suffolk accent 'We got laammb today'. The toolpusher flew into a rage and shouted that it wasn't fit for oilmen and demanded that it be thrown off the rig and steak was to be for dinner. Following which the toolpusher stormed out.

Fig. 7.3 *Jack-up Britannia, operated by Santa Fe, drilling Conoco/NCB 49/17-8.*

Following discussions with Cookie, some roustabouts and myself, the geologist, all of whom were rather partial to roast lamb, hatched a plan within the radio room in which the offending limbs would be fished from the seas by standby trawler and delivered surreptitiously back onboard. The deal was that the trawler crew would also benefit from a leg of lamb. The feast that followed was memorable in more ways than one".

To give ewe another example of offshore culinary conundrums, John Church adds:

"This incident recalls to mind an experience that I had on the discovery well in Beryl.

The rig that drilled the first well was the Glomar V a small (250' long) drill ship which had been brought into the North Sea for the summer of 1972 from some West African country. Whilst on location a small whaler appeared alongside and requested some medical assistance which was duly supplied. As a token of their appreciation they donated a chunk of whalemeat for our 'gourmet restaurant'. Incidentally, I fondly remember the Glomar V as having one of the best canteens that I have tried in my (albeit limited) experience. In those pre-Greenpeace days, and before British consciousness was raised over difficult environmental issues, most of us, who hadn't experienced speck (or whale meat) in the governments 'Utility' restaurants after the war were looking forward to tasting unusual food. Unfortunately the meat had to mature for 24 hours and it was left on deck and, yes you've guessed it, someone in the shape of a toolpusher or even a budding Greenpeace roustabout (were there such people???) hoofed it into the drink.

That was my closest encounter with a whaler and whalemeat despite numerous subsequent visits to Norway."

Perhaps we are digressing slightly, but it is important to remember that everyone's key offshore memories are different; for every success story we quote there were many other dry holes and work offshore did not necessarily guarantee the glamour of a discovery or even your favourite food! There are many stories to tell which simply reflect day-to-day rig occurrences - some possibly bizarre by today's standards of stringent offshore practice guidelines and rigorous health and safety directives.

Post Fourth Round, however, with the Brent area and Viking Graben coming into sharp focus, the Jurassic became an excellent reservoir to chase. Myles Bowen continues looking at some of the key developments through the seventies and some of the new plays that were found, accidentally or otherwise:

"The Fourth Round, by opening up the Brent area and Viking Graben opened up the next, by far largest play, the Jurassic - mainly the Middle Jurassic.

The 'golden block', 211/21 turned out to be somewhat disappointing as the Jurassic reservoir was thinly developed over shallow basement. Nevertheless, the two Cormorant Fields with combined reserves of over 600 mmbbl must have long since recouped Shell/Esso their original stake.

A string of Middle Jurassic (some including Triassic) discoveries followed, notably Ninian and Beryl on the UK side and the super-giant 3.6 bnbbl Statfjord Field on the Brent extension in Norway.

The Fourth Round was less spectacular in the Central and Southern North Sea as the majority of blocks had already been allocated in the first three Rounds. Nevertheless yet another new play was established on Fourth Round acreage to the northwest of Forties in the Witch Ground graben when Occidental hit the jackpot with discoveries in Upper Jurassic reservoirs at Piper and Claymore which had initial reserves of 950 and 490 mmbbl respectively. Oxy was a newcomer to the North Sea and made these discoveries on blocks which had not been highly rated by the established explorers.

However accomplished, serendipity continued to play a large part to my knowledge. For instance, when Shell was forced for logistic reasons to find a southerly location for the Staflo rig in October 1975 the only available prospect had been on the books for some time, but looked too puny to be worthwhile drilling. The target was Middle to Upper Jurassic sandstone in a small structural closure just east of the Auk horst; 50- 120 mmbbl was a likely outcome, assuming any Jurassic sand was present. In fact, the well found 1000 ft of sand, 600 ft of oil column, and reserves approaching 500 mmbbl; thus the Fulmar play was initiated.

Immediately after drilling the Brent discovery well, Shell drilled 16/8-1, on a promising 3rd Round block. The well tested structural closure from the Palaeocene downwards but only found oil in thin poorly developed sands in the Upper Jurassic which tested at 1200 barrels per day. Shell's explorers called it a discovery and referred to it as 'Cormorant', until the engineers told them it was non commercial and the name was reserved for the next discovery which turned out to be on 211/21, the 'golden block'.

At about this time we were offered the opportunity to farmin to the adjacent block 16/7. Examination of the seismic suggested that the Upper Jurassic consisted of proximal alluvial fans deposited against a major fault scarp comprised of Devonian sandstones and shales. Only one small dip-closed feature was present, so what was required for a large field was an updip fault/strat trap of the fan against the Devonian of the East Shetland platform. After examining as many analogues as we could find in the company's files, we concluded that the fans would contain boulders in a poorly sorted sand/silt/ mud matrix, hardly a viable reservoir. Also we doubted that the Devonian on the footwall would provide a seal. So we turned down the farmout which turned out to be the 550 mmbl Brae Field, yet another new play-type. What we had also failed to predict was that beween the 'ratty' distal sands of 16/8-1 and the conglomeratic proximal fans of Brae (our prognosis having been largely correct) lay the excellent quality reservoirs now exemplified in the Miller Field, a relatively low area later relinquished by the licensees on both sides and picked up later by Conoco/Saxon and BP.

Oxy's successful exploration in the Witch Ground Graben included discovery of oil in deeper mass-flow sands of the Claymore Formation lying within the Kimmeridge shales. These good quality sands, embedded in the source formation, were the most likely reservoir to be sourced in the entire North Sea, little migration being necessary.

A similar deep water fan forms the Magnus reservoir at the northern end of the East

Shetland Basin. Block 211/12 was favoured by Shell in the Fourth Round because of its internal reflections (signifying middle Jurassic) but it was allocated to BP who liked it for its large Palaeocene closure. In the event it turned out that both protagonists were wrong. There was no Palaeocene sand and the oil was in unsuspected late Jurassic sands and not in the middle Jurassic Brent".

Mention is made above of the Brae Field - indeed, turned down by Shell at the time a farm-in was offered. Perhaps to expand a little on its discovery, an account by Clive Randle (below), describes in some detail some of the key entrepreneurial steps taken at that time up the stairway to success:

"The Third Round of Licensing attracted a large number of smaller companies to participate in applications for blocks and many were successful. These companies succeeded (or failed) on the strength of the entrepreneurial skills of their principals. It is possible that today similar companies would not meet some of the criteria for the award of a licence. In 1970 two small companies Syracuse Oil, founded by a Canadian business man, Angus A. Mackenzie, and Pan Ocean Oil Corporation a company created by Louis Marx of Marx Toys, were awarded Licence P108 comprising Blocks 16/3 and 16/7. Shortly afterwards, in 1970, Syracuse was amalgamated with fellow Canadian company Bow Valley Industries Ltd (now part of Talisman Energy Inc.) which had been founded in 1950 by D K 'Doc' Seaman. The participants in the group grew to include Siebens Oil and Gas, founded by Bill Siebens, Sunningdale Oils, another Angus Mackenzie off-shoot and (through Martin Siem of Fred Olsen) there were Norwegian interests which eventually were held by Saga Petroleum at the time of the discovery. Here was a combination of strong personalities with personal wealth at stake, willing to take risk in the further creation of wealth. As anyone might imagine, not a formula for eternal harmony and contentment but common interest became the mediator. Adding a different dimension to the group's deliberations, the National Coal Board held an option to back-in to the Licence with 20% equity on a commercial discovery which allowed it to participate as an observer in the early stages. It is not possible to see behind each of these companies but as an illustration of the levels of risk undertaken, the involvement of Bow Valley is a typical example.

By 1973 the seismic surveys had been shot over Licence P 108 and the technical representatives of the companies had made their maps. Then came the dilemma. A closure was mapped in the western part of Block 16/7 on an event attributed to the Palaeocene sands (West Brae). With the discovery of Forties Field, was this the best target? In the northern part of the Block 16/7 there was a deep target, possibly with sediments of Jurassic age (North Brae). Shell had recently tested oil from well 16/8-1 but information was held very tightly so, with nothing to trade, the group could only speculate. The results coming from the Jurassic in the Quadrant 211 blocks were encouraging for the deeper prospect option but the closure and assumed reservoir thickness combined with the depth raised doubts about the economic viability of the prospect. The Palaeocene test would be much cheaper to drill. This is when the common aims of the partners diverged. Each partner in different ways had commitments outside of Licence P108 and each was carefully balancing the risk, the reward and the capital expenditure required. The personal stakes of the founders of the companies were on the line. What would persuade them to agree?

In the early seventies that most persuasive of tools was entering the seismic market - colour. Seiscom-Delta had already developed its Seischrome presentation of data which incorporated early DHI techniques. A trial processing of lines over the licence showed bright yellows and reds across the Palaeocene structure - Gas? The balance of interest began to tip away from the Palaeocene on technical grounds, but the well cost remained a point in its favour. Bow Valley's Senior Vice-President, Dick Harris and Fred Wellhauser, the Exploration Manager, listened to the views of the explorationists of the companies involved and were persuaded to take the proposal to drill the Jurassic prospect to Doc Seaman and the board of Bow Valley. Bow Valley had a 35 per cent interest in the licence and their share of the estimated cost of the well represented a significant part of its revenue. The well was approved on the condition that the Odin Drill would be used for the operations. Subsequently, the other partners were also persuaded, to accept what was, for each of them, a high exposure.

Pan Ocean spudded the first well 16/7-1 on 19 September 1974, at which time Shell agreed to the pre-trade release of the data from well 16/8-1. Cold comfort - the Jurassic sands were thin and 'ratty'. The Odin Drill was on only its second well since commissioning and suffered from the extreme weather of the winter of 1974/75 and experienced mechanical failures particularly related to the BOPE. It was on location over 230 days and the well cost had more than doubled to US$16 million to reach the TD of 15,695 feet (one of the North Sea's most expensive wells for many years). Bow Valley's share of the cost of the well consumed most of the company's discretionary cash flow during the period. It had been a harrowing time for the entrepreneurs, exacerbated by one daily telex from the Odin Drill stating that the well had penetrated the Kimmeridge Clay, had encountered thin 'Middle' Jurassic sands and these were water wet; consequently no coring was justified a message likely to turn the faint hearted. The group carried on to drill the full, potentially prospective section. The reward did not come from the deeper section but from those 'Middle' Jurassic sands which electric logs showed to be hydrocarbon saturated through a gross column of 500 feet. This placed the oil-water contact outside the mapped closure of the structure. The well eventually flowed at a rate in excess of 22,000 bopd. A reward that repaid the 'guts' of those entrepreneurs.

For those small companies the three discovery wells in the Brae Area became a mixed blessing. Having found the money to explore successfully, the task of finding the development funds, particularly in a political climate of 'state participation' when the NCB became part of the BNOC, was equally challenging for them. Some succumbed to take-overs or sold-out, others chose different routes to finance. Bow Valley decided to stay as a participant in the project and devised a variation on a farm-out arrangement it had previously negotiated for its Mackenzie Delta lands in Northern Canada. The essence of the deal was that the farminee paid back-costs, funded all of Bow Valley's share of the development costs, Bow Valley retained 30% of the net proceeds of production from half of its original equity interest in the licences, the other half being assigned to the farminee. Some said that this was the 'sweetest farm-out of all', others would disagree! However, it was a linchpin for the progress and growth of Bow Valley".

2. **The Irish Sea**

We have now covered, in varying degrees of detail, many of the key milestones in the early years of North Sea history - relative depth of coverage reflecting directly their importance to our panel of contributors. But the North Sea was not the only British offshore environment gaining attention in the early years - indeed, the Irish Sea (and in particular, events leading up to the discovery of the Morecambe Gas Field) had shown steady exploration progress since 1965. Vic Colter provides us with the following account:

"The first licences in the Irish Sea were awarded to the Gulf/National Coal Board partnership in 1965, during the Second Round. Two wells were drilled by this group in 1969, namely 110/8-1 and 110/8-2. The first spudded into the Sherwood Sandstone and bottomed in the Carboniferous, whilst the second spudded into the Mercia Mudstones and bottomed in the Carboniferous. Both were abandoned as dry.

Fig. 7.4 *Platform on the Morecambe Bay Field.*

In 1969, as part of the Third Round, the Socialist government of the day was anxious to foster British nationalised industry presence in hydrocarbon exploration and exploitation. As part of this plan, it was decreed that:

a) The Gas Council could hold licences 100% in its own name in the Irish Sea and Cardigan Bay.
b) Other licensees had at least to offer an option to participate to either the Gas Council or the NCB, in these waters.

In the Third Round, the Gas Council and Amoco had an AMI over the areas in which licences were offered. Gas Council staff saw the Irish Sea as the North Sea writ small. We expected, or at least hoped for, gas of Carboniferous origin in the Permian Collyhurst Sandstone, and sealed by the Zechstein equivalent in the shape of the Manchester Marls.

Seismic had been shot by the Gas Council/Amoco group, and interpreted by both partners. Various structures were seen by the Gas Council, in particular a large egg-shaped structure on Block 110/7. Gas Council management insisted that in any licence application a firm well had to be offered. Amoco, having other priorities, rejected such extravagance.

During this discussion, a fundamental difference between the Gas Council and Amoco interpretations emerged. On the Western side of the Irish Sea Basin, where the Permo-Trias section was wedging out by erosion, deeper, east-dipping events were seen. Amoco's geophysicist, sent in from the Gulf Coast of USA, interpreted these events as being evidence of an additional western half-graben, and boldly put in a large, down-to-the-west fault. The Gas Council geophysicists, under Peter Thompsett, had seen the same deeper events in the analogous Cheshire Basin, where it was clear that they were Carboniferous reflectors, appearing where the Permo-Trias overburden had thinned. Furthermore, the IGS in 1968 had taken sea-bed samples of Carboniferous age from the area where these events subcropped, whose existence was known to me.

Amoco wished to make an application for licences in this area, offering only a conditional well. Considerable discussion ensued, concerning the exact significance of the seismic and the sea-bed sample. To settle these differences of interpretation, the Gas Council tried to charter the vessel used by the IGS, the good ship Whitethorn, from Wimpey to take further samples. In the event, bad weather intervened and prevented sampling in time to influence the application.

In its efforts to secure another partner who would commit to a well, the Gas Council made a presentation to the Conoco manager of the day. My recollection is that he sat through the presentation with a look on his face saying 'You're not impressing me'. Conoco found the offered 50% interest to be easily resistible.

The Gas Council management showed its confidence in its fledgling staff, or its desire to impress government, by making a successful sole risk application in the Third Round for blocks that included the, then, prized 110/7 block, but nothing over what became the Morecambe Field. Amoco applied for a swathe of blocks to the west, which it was awarded. In 1970, after the awards, IGS resumed its sea-bed sampling programme with the Whitethorn, and demonstrated that Amoco's acreage lay on or about the Palaeozoic Isle of Man/Anglesey Ridge. It did not have an obligation well, though!

In the Fourth Round, the Gas Council acquired Block 110/2, its first acreage over the Morecambe accumulation, and continued its refinement of the seismic mapping, still directing its attention to the bottom of the Permo-Trias section.

Sometime in 1972, or thereabouts, Gulf invited us in to consider a farm-in proposal on Block 110/8. They revealed a mud log and other data that indicated a gas kick and shows over some tens of feet of the top Sherwood Sandstone. This bothersome high pressure had been speedily controlled during drilling by weighting up the mud, and the shows had obligingly disappeared. The deal was that we should drill a well in satisfaction of an outstanding obligation. I have no memory of where this well might have been drilled, but we agreed to farm-in. The then licensing authority thought otherwise, as the obligation had already been shifted from the North Sea. We were not so disappointed at this outcome, as the glimpse of Gulf's mud log had shown us that on our own acreage we could get three hundred feet, or so, updip from the gas shows in the Sherwood Sandstone. Nevertheless, attention was still centred on the independent 'egg' on Block 110/7.

Suddenly in March 1973, the Gulf manager, who was at lunch with Peter Hinde, offered to let us have the logs of the Gulf/NCB wells in the Irish Sea, in return for the logs of any well we might drill. No formal trade was concluded, the basis of the exchange being merely a gentleman's agreement. The full composite log of 110/8-2 showed us, for the first time, that the 'Collyhurst Sandstone', our erstwhile target formation, appeared to be developed as a shale. We were, therefore, stuck with the gas shows in the Sherwood as our only lead.

The wireline logs were sent by Peter Hinde to John Bains, Hydrocarbons Great Britain's (HGB's) log analyst, who admits that he assigned a low priority to them, in view of the fact that they were from four year old abandonments, and that there was no immediate pressure to devise a logging programme for the planned 110/7-1 well. John finally looked at them in July 1973, and concluded that there was a 600 foot hydrocarbon column in well 110/8-2, with a GWC at -3750 feet. In the absence of a Neutron log, it was not possible to say whether the pore-fluid was oil or gas, although the latter seemed more likely.

Since the logs came HGB's way as part of a gentleman's agreement, Peter Hinde phoned Gulf to tell them of John's interpretation. At the same time, the Department of Energy was informed. Gulf's interpretation had been carried out by computer in the Houston headquarters, where the calculations were re-run, with the same result: 'water bearing'. I believe that at or about the same time the Department of Energy carried out their own analysis, their interpretation agreeing with John's. By this time, it became important to find out who was right. Various colourful stories, involving a 'make-up-your-minds' shootout between John and Gulf's man in a locked room, were current about these discussions. John tells me that nothing so melodramatic happened. Suffice it to say that eventually Gulf agreed with him.

The reason for the incorrect interpretation by Gulf, as told to Peter Hinde, was at least twofold. In the first place, an incorrect R_W was used for the highly saline connate water. The second, and more significant, error involved a pair of scissors. Log-run 1 went down to about the base of the Mercia Mudstones (top of the Sherwood Sandstone), and run 2 started at top Sherwood level. Apparently, someone cut the heading off the run 2 log and stuck it on the bottom of the run 1 log, not noticing a scale change in the resistivity readings. I have since heard a story concerning some involvement of a highly resistive, thin anhydrite at the base of the Mercia Mudstones (top reservoir), but cannot substantiate this. Of course, when Gulf Houston re-ran their calculations, they re-ran them using the same numbers with the same basic errors, and with the same outcome.

Having met the requirement to honour the gentlemanly aspect of the gift by Gulf of the logs, Peter Hinde then contacted Gulf about the possibility of a farm-in to Block 110/8. I well remember a visit by a representative of Gulf's partner, NCB. The gist of the meeting was that it would indeed be splendid if HGB were to farm-in, as the Gulf/NCB partnership had, a month or so back, given notice of intent to surrender the block. An approach to the Department of Energy requesting a farm-in was turned down, as notice of intent to surrender was regarded as intent, unless new data had become available. So, for a couple of months Gulf/NCB had to watch Block 110/8 evaporate before their eyes.

1974 saw the re-election of a Labour Government, with Tony Benn i/c Energy. In those days, with that government at least, nationalised industries could apply for unallocated blocks between formal licensing rounds. HGB applied for, and was awarded, Blocks 110/3 and 110/8.

It might be thought twenty years on that John's triumph of man over computer in the of exploration all that much, given that HGB already had Block 110/2 on the accumulation, and might have acquired Blocks 110/3 and 110/8 by normal means in a licensing round. The really significant influence was, however, that until John's re-interpretation, HGB was going to drill the large and apparently simple egg-shaped structure in Block 110/7.

In fact, it took Peter Hinde about three months to convince the General Manager, Exploration Companies, an engineer, that adherence to Hinde's First Law, i.e.

moving from the known to the unknown, had more to recommend it than the beguiling structure on 110/7.

In the event we successfully drilled our obligation well on Block 110/2, on trend with 110/8-2, and eventually a second dry hole on the 'egg' on Block 110/7. I am more than half convinced that had we not had Gulf's gift of logs and John's interpretation of them, and had drilled the obligation well as a dry hole on Block 110/7, then it would have taken more than wild horses to have secured approval for an early second well in the basin, especially on-trend with the otherwise apparently dry 110/8-2, gas-show notwithstanding.

Well 110/2-1 was, in fact, something of a disappointment. It produced gas from several tests at non-commercial rates and was, as John Bains says, the only non-commercial well on the Morecambe Field. Subsequent drilling showed that part of the better Keuper Sandstone (as we called it then) reservoir was cut out by a fault.

As an indication of how well this success in the Irish Sea was communicated to the population at large, I vividly remember, in 1974 or 1975, visiting my in-laws in the North. On entering a room, I saw the face of a British Gas PR man, filling the TV screen. One unusual aspect of this apparition was, however, that he was wearing a helmet saying 'AMOCO'. I said to my wife 'what on earth is this?' She said 'Oh, Amoco's doing something in the Irish Sea'. Can you imagine the fate of any Amoco equivalent who appeared in a British Gas helmet? These were the same public interfacers who offered to sell me a plastic cube with Wytch Farm oil, and who reportedly told the public at the Knutsford No 1 site that 'These rocks were laid down several years ago'.

Fig. 7.5 *Drilling in other areas - the ship Hardrill drilling BP's first well 93/2-1 in the Celtic Sea/St George's Channel 1974.*

Despite the confusion created in my wife's mind by the TV appearance of the Amoco helmet (as a result of lack of confidence in the Irish Sea play on the part of two major oil companies, plus the errors of another), the nationalised HGB came to control the Morecambe Field - the first operated venture of its exploration team. It is worthwhile remembering that John's log interpretation could not conclusively say whether oil or gas was present. Had it been oil, then it would not only have been huge, but would have gone down the Swanee along with the other oil assets in the early 1980's, before the brainwave of privatising the gas industry as a whole entered the collective political mind.

A final digression into the origin of the field's name may be permissible at this point. Increasingly, one hears it referred to as 'Morecambe Bay', by relative newcomers. In fact, the name was originally thought up by Peter Hinde, who followed the established practice in the Southern North Sea and took the name from that of a nearby sea-bed feature called 'Morecambe Bank'.

When the field was first discovered, Peter told me one day that Mr Rooke (now Sir Dennis) had said that a field in the Irish Sea should have a name with an Irish flavour. Having been born north of the Mersey, I took exception to this and wrote a memo to Peter noting that the nearest landfall was in the County Palatine of Lancaster (or what was left of it).

I suggested that we follow the precedent set by the naming of the Formby Field, and that we name it after another Lancastrian entertainer and call it the 'Gracie Field'. Peter says he passed this memo on to Mr Rooke, but I never got a reply.

Anyway, eventually the field did end up bearing the name of a great north-country entertainer."

Figs. 7.6 to 7.8 illustrate the status of The United Kingdom's exploration drilling and the resultant discoveries which had been made at the beginning of 1979. Both onshore (see next chapter) and offshore exploration wells are shown along with the actual fields in production by 1979. It is interesting to compare these diagrams with a later suite (in chapter ten) bringing us up to date sixteen years later in 1994/1995.

Fig. 7.6
Exploration wells
(as of end 1978)

Fig. 7.7
Discoveries at end of 1978.

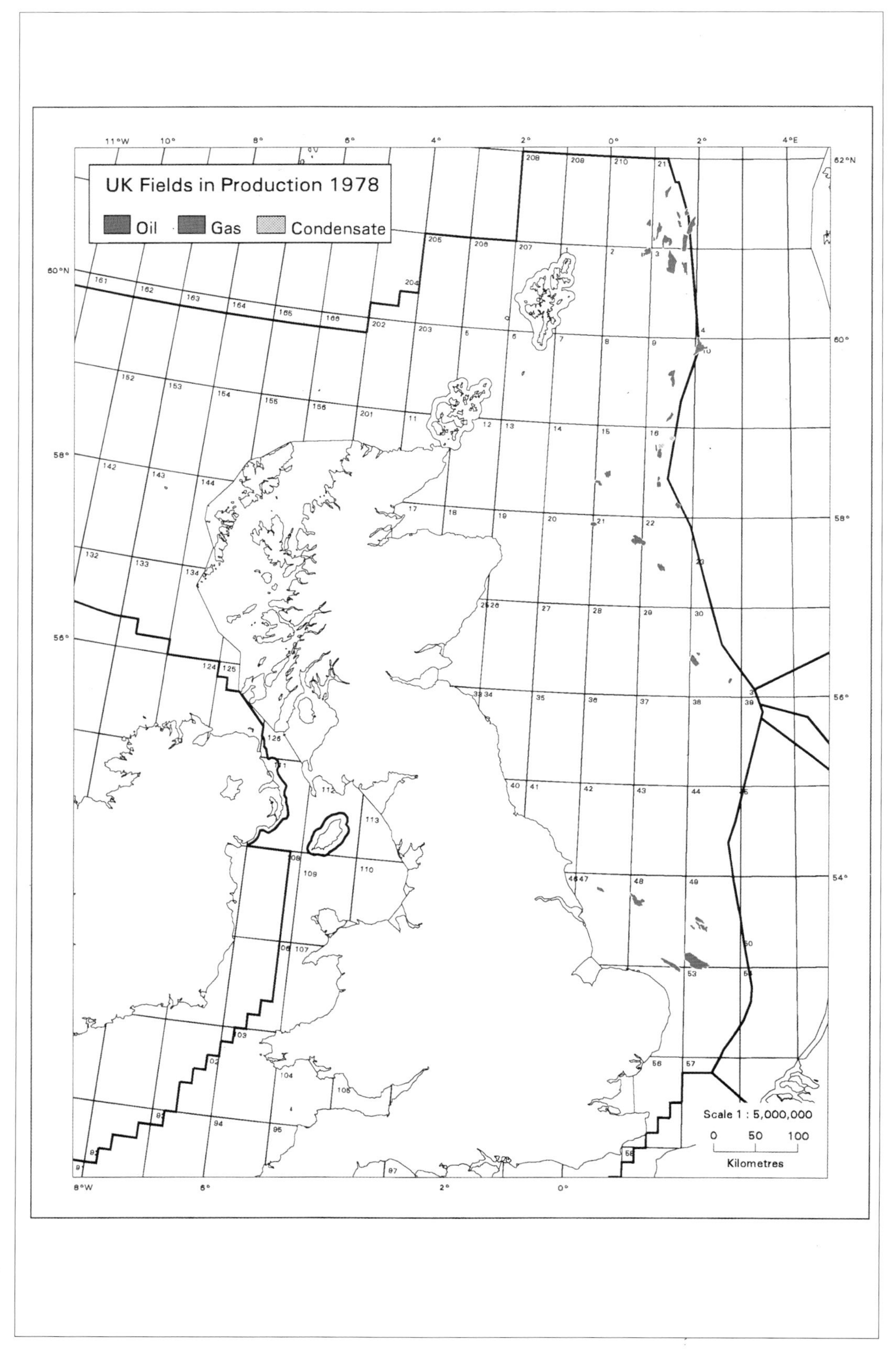

Fig. 7.8
UK Fields in Production (1978)

Chapter Eight

Efforts Back Onshore

With all our attention thus far being focused on the offshore, it is appropriate to remind ourselves that the drill bit had not ceased to function on land while all the dramas of the first four rounds were unfolding. Far from it, in fact it should be remembered that it was onshore geology in the first place that led to some of the earliest offshore ideas - even though the extrapolations from Yorkshire to Holland were rather simplified! Also the legislation had already been established for onshore exploration long before the Geneva Convention and the Continental Shelf Act of 1964 - in fact the first onshore well was drilled as long ago as 1918 (just after the First World War) at Hardstoft in Derbyshire. Eventually a licensing system was set up with the introduction of the Petroleum Production Act of 1934. Peter Hinde explains what happened:

"Drilling was started in 1936 (at Portsdown, Hampshire) by British Petroleum (then d'Arcy Exploration Company). Two years before, the Petroleum Act of 1934 had secured for the Crown all rights to petroleum. The first discoveries of importance were of gas, at Cousland near Edinburgh and at Eskdale near Whitby. In 1939 came the first of the several small oilfields in the Nottingham area which were developed rapidly for the purposes of war, as the following output figures show:-

1939 - 3,577 tons
1943 - 113,000 tons
1963 - 122,800 tons
1965 - 127,000 tons

Included here, of course, was the Eakring Dukeswood oilfield of Nottinghamshire (see Fig. 8.1) which last produced in 1971. Production from this peaked at around 1600 bopd in 1941 with a cumulative total recovery of about 6.5 mmbbls.

Peter Hinde continues:

"In 1952 the Gas Council (GC) joined forces with BP in the search for natural gas and also for structures underground suitable for the storage of peak load gas.

Three prospects were found. At Calow in Derbyshire a gas field was located which has since been produced for local consumption. Natural gas was also found at Trumfleet in Yorkshire and at Ironville in Nottinghamshire, the former of which was also found to contain oil during further drilling in 1965."

But all these finds were clearly fairly small and encouragement restricted, with only a few key players still in the game. A particularly interesting story involves the discovery of the Lockton Gas accumulation, for which the GC and the Canadian company Home Oil take varying degrees of credit. Vic Colter has written the following account of how he recalls events unfolding:

Fig. 8.1
Testing the water content of an Eakring oil well (1959)

"The GC and its successor British Gas have been associated with many notable exploration successes, both as operator and non-operator, since the earliest days of modern exploration.

In 1965, Home Oil of Canada embarked on the drilling of a series of interest-earning wells on licences in the North Yorkshire Moors area. These licences, part of a group extending through Holderness and into Lincolnshire, were held in trust by BP on behalf of the GC, which was apparently unable to hold licences in its own name at that time.

BP had found gas in the Zechstein in two wells at Eskdale in North Yorks. One produced from the Upper Magnesian Limestone, and the other from a short penetration of a deeper horizon. Gas from one or both of these wells was fed for a time into the Whitby gas works, where it was diluted or reformed into low BTU town gas. My first awareness of this operation was when, in about 1963, I was with Shell in the Netherlands and heard via the BBC that a well had blown out at Eskdale.

Each of the wells drilled by Home had a contract or interest-earning depth, defined in stratigraphic terms and negotiated by BP. This was commonly the penetration of the Upper Magnesian Limestone, but in some cases a deeper horizon was specified. The GC had the right to participate for its remaining 50% in any deepening operations. In the event that the GC did not participate, and gas was found, a 400% penalty clause operated, if the Council wished to retain an interest in the accumulation.

In 1965, Home drilled a well, Lockton 2a, close to an earlier shallow Jurassic hole of BP's. The contract depth was to penetrate the Upper Magnesian Limestone, which proved water-bearing. Home decided to deepen, and notified the GC of its right to participate. The story was that the Council, having participated in the deepening of (I think) Rosedale No 1 and found nothing, decided not to exercise its right.

Home went ahead and deepened, finding 400+ feet of gas pay in a thick carbonate unit, which tested at very impressive rates. The GC, naturally, wished to participate and the penalty clause came into operation.

At this time I was on an assignment with Shell Canada, to find out how the recent carbonate research I had been dragooned into was applied in practice. (I soon found that it wasn't, as we never had the time, and it didn't 'buy us any boots', as my manager said). My recollection is that the Albertan press gave the impression that Home had just about saved the British economy. Little thinking that I should ever have any involvement, I produced my North Yorks Regional Guide, and showed it round the office, to let at least the Shell Canadians know that we already knew about these 'reefs', and in any case BP had production close by at Eskdale, so there!

The gas-bearing formation in Lockton, occurring between the Upper Magnesian Limestone and an apparent Lower Magnesian Limestone, was immediately called the 'Middle Mag'. This incorrect nomenclature was ineradicable, and gave rise to all sorts of etymological sports, such as 'Middle Magnesian Evaporites'. I believe that the first person to identify the unit correctly was Dr John Taylor of V C Illing & Partners, who was carrying out a study for BP and the GC. John showed that this was the carbonate part of the second Zechstein cycle (ZII), not present at the outcrop. The true Middle Magnesian Limestone of the outcrop is part of the ZI cycle. John's recognition of the foresetting nature of these ZI and ZII carbonates and evaporites was first published in a letter to 'Nature' in 1970, jointly with George Fong of Home, and later in a joint paper he and I wrote in the first North Sea conference (1975). The unit is now called the Kirkham Abbey Formation.

The Lockton reservoir was commonly referred to as a 'reef', but John quickly demonstrated that it was, in fact, a very fine-grained dolomitised wackestone, in the Dunham classification. (It was later invoked as 'high energy wackestone', a terminological impossibility, in the BP recommendation to drill Egton High Moor No 1, the updip seal of which was postulated to be the shelfward oolites, elsewhere proposed as a reservoir e.g. Malton No. 1.) The perceived high production potential of the reservoir in Lockton resulted from the pervasive presence of fractures. This potential was to prove something of an illusion.

Subsequent wells Lockton No's. 3, 4 and 5 all proved dry, the reservoir being both lower and thinner than in Lockton No. 2a. The thinner reservoir was compensated by thicker evaporites, lying between the carbonates and the overlying Upper-Mag. Lockton was, in reality, a carbonate mound or bank of some sort.

This was the situation that I found when I escaped from Shell, and became a 'carbonate geologist' with the GC, in August 1967. (I kept quiet about it's not 'buying any boots'.) As an aside at this point, Peter Walmsley's account of his early North Sea days records his pleasure at being offered the princely salary of £2,100 per annum by BP on returning to the UK at 37 years of age in 1965. My 'Sterling Pensionable Salary' on leaving Shell at 36 years in 1967 was £2,400 per year. In those days, this salary was academic, that is until you drew a pension based on it, as you were never in the UK. I was, therefore, delighted to have been offered £2,740 on Band E of the Senior Officers Table by the GC.

My first job with the GC was far removed from carbonate geology. My next involvement was with the Lockton 6 location-picking meeting. The previous wells had been located on 'Vibroseis' data, and all were drilled on convincing-looking 'highs' at a Zechstein level. Lockton No 6 was proposed on a similar feature. It was apparent to me, although seemingly not so obvious to some, that whatever level the 'highs' at Lockton No 3, 4 and 5 were at, they did not reflect the form of the top of the reservoir, so why should that be proposed for well No 6? This point was argued interminably, but such was the seductive power of the seismic that we either acquiesced, or were outvoted by Home and BP (who were present because they were coming in for half of GC interests in the northern licences in general, see below).

In the event, Lockton No 6 had the deepest, thinnest representation of the reservoir of any of the wells. It was obvious that, at best, the seismic was mapping the Upper Mag, and there was a suspicion that the form of this reflector had as much to do with topography as anything else. At this point, I did a thumbnail structure map at top reservoir level, using well tops, and showed that the direction to go was east. This was not really very clever, because that was about the only direction left. Lockton No 7 was located east of the discovery, and came in with a lower, thinner reservoir, but with 100+ feet of pay.

Somewhere in all this process, the old licences were re-negotiated and issued as 'new' PL's, whose boundaries gave a little more recognition to the National Grid, and less to parish boundaries. At the same time BP, sensing the importance of gas, let the GC into its southern oil-prone licences for 50%, in return for a 50% interest in the gas-prone blocks. Lockton, having been found before this re-negotiation, remained a GC interest, and the 'Lockton Rectangle' was drawn round the accumulation, within which the interests were Home 50%, GC 50%.

Since reservoir geometry was obviously rather poorly known, in order to arrive at some sort of reserve figure, production tests were carried out. Equally obviously, these results produced a variety of views on the significance of inflection points on graphs, and therefore a variety of reserve figures. Home's preferred figure was in excess of 400 BCF, based on the belief that the inflection points represented distances to accumulation boundaries, enabling volumetric estimates to be made. The GC, in the person of Martin Ford, thought that about a quarter of this was a more prudent figure, based on the preliminary linear rate of decline of reservoir pressure during an extended test. In the event, for plant-sizing and other considerations, the Home Oil International oil-men's views seemed to be more convincing, or more beguiling, to the GC management than those of its own fugitives from the mainstream oil industry. Neither of these figures proved to be anything like the economically recoverable reserves.

The Zechstein gas was sour, and a decision was taken to use a process licensed by an Italian company, which apparently used arsenic as a catalyst. At about the same time, the GC was advertising its own 'Stretford Process', named for the suburb of Manchester where it was invented. For some reason this was not a front-runner for the Lockton plant.

With the larger reserve figure and the test production rates in mind, construction of an office and a plant with two 100 MMCFD streams was put in hand at Pickering. As a not-altogether-successful sop to the reluctant inhabitants of the town, a play-ground was offered for their children. In autumn 1970, flushed with success, Home called the annual Work Programme and Budget meeting in Calgary, after which we all took off for a weekend in the Rockies, staying in log cabins at the Jasper Park Lodge, where an earlier Prince of Wales had stayed. We were also entertained in the hospitality suite in the Brown Building in Calgary, with its amazing Ranch House - Rococo - Provencal - Gothic decor.

In May 1971, the plant and office were ready, and a grand opening ceremony planned. We all went up by BR to Pickering, and on the train met Mr Brown Jr, President of Home and his brother-in-law, the Chief of Police of Calgary. Present in the marquee were Lord Beatty, Chairman of Home in the UK, the Lord Lieutenant of the County in his 'best blue' uniform and a number of token locals. The Chief of Police of Calgary behaved like any good security man should, handing the dignitaries in and out of their cars, and generally standing back and keeping an eye on the dubious-looking revellers. After a few words, Lord Beatty proposed that we 'uncork

Fig. 8.2
The Pickering Gas Processing Plant.

the bottled lightning' and get on with it, a sentiment that seemed to find favour with guests.

After lunch, a few speeches were made, including some by locals whose latent hostility was scarcely disguised. One started by saying 'I was going to say 'Good old Home Oil', but ...'. Later, we went on a guided tour of the plant and office. These benefited from the expertise of the GC favourite outside design consultants, and it has to be said that a splendid job had been done. I particularly remember a volcano-like sculpture/landscape feature, constructed from cobblestones, in a patio of the offices.

This was the first and only time I ever visited the plant, and the last time I visited Pickering. The gloss was taken off the whole opening ceremony by the fact that about two weeks later, Lockton No 7, the deeper well, started to produce water. I cannot remember the exact chronology, but some time later the discovery well started showing similar symptoms. Lengthy opening up and shutting in exercises were carried out, hoping that the water, which was coming up the fractures, would fall back, but it didn't. Attempts at numerical simulation, based on the limited production history were used in a vain attempt to arrive at a better reserve figure. To make matters worse, water somehow got into the heavy hydrocarbon absorption vessel and caused foaming. To make things even worse, although in the end academic, the recovered sulphur proved to be contaminated by the arsenic used in the process, and was not only unsaleable, but represented a disposal problem. It was even suggested that it might be quietly dumped in the Bay of Biscay. (As far as I know, this never happened, so the tuna is probably OK). The whole operation was eventually shut down, and the plant mothballed.

In the meantime, GC geophysicists, under Peter Thompsett, thought that they had cracked the problem of mapping the Lockton reservoir top, and proposed a well to test a separate target a few miles south of Lockton, at Wykeham. The well found the reservoir to be gas-bearing, but it proved impossible on test to produce gas without formation brine.

It seemed, then, that the bimodal porosity/permeability system of high porosity, low permeability dolomite and extensive fracturing meant that, certainly at the production rates attempted at Lockton, water almost inevitably by-passed matrix gas. One cannot help speculating on what might have happened had lower initial production rates been used. In the event, the difference between Home's and GC reserves became academic, as recoverable reserves were a fraction of either.

This Lockton disappointment, plus further drilling disappointments and continuing seismic problems led first BP and later, reluctantly, the GC to withdraw from the onshore Zechstein play entirely, about 20 years ago. We had other fish to fry, albeit temporarily as it turned out, at Wytch Farm.

Others seem since to have had success in the oolite belt shelfward of Lockton, in the Malton area, where seismic reflectors always more closely represented reservoir structure, but it remains to be seen when or whether the Lockton water will ever fall back in the fracture system. I remember that a group operated by Taylor Woodrow drilled a well east of Lockton in 1980, and also remember how their house magazine proudly showed on its cover a photograph of the well with a big flame, but also with a copious spray of water.

So, at least at that date and as far as I know to this present day, Lockton remains one of life's great 'might have been's'. It was a fortunate thing for all of us, from the bread and butter point of view, that a few other things came along to replace Lockton. I was able to escape from the more academic 'carbonate geologist' cul de sac, and to earn a few boots in the UK onshore and elsewhere, albeit that for the most part others ended up wearing them."

But certainly, the Permian Magnesian limestone onshore UK continued to receive detailed exploration interest - particularly during the mid 1980's with for example, the discovery of Kirkby Misperton by Taylor Woodrow (now Kelt) in 1984.

However, (with perhaps the exception of some of BP's East Midlands discoveries) most people immediately associate success onshore with the Wytch Farm oilfield in Dorset. Technical accounts of this have been published elsewhere, but, to complete the record, Vic Colter provides us with this original review of the key issues and behind-the-scenes dramas at the time:

"When I joined the GC in August 1967, the re-issuing of a number of old licences as 'new' Production Licences was awaited. BP had been active in the area since before the war, and had made discoveries at Kimmeridge (1959) and Wareham (1964). The productive capacity of the latter remained untested.

The new PL's were finally awarded in 1968, with a work commitment of one well on PL's 086-088 in the Hants Basin and six stratigraphic tests to top Jurassic on PL's 089- 091 in the Wessex Basin. As best I remember it, the objective of the stratigraphic tests was to map the Jurassic sub-crop and the pinch-out of the Wealden to the west.

Shapwick and Woodlands were drilled in 1968 in partial fulfilment of this stratigraphic obligation.

Whilst mulling over the aims and results of this programme, it occurred to me that even if we knew why we were interested in these pinch-outs and sub-crops, another four holes were not going to add a great deal of precision to our knowledge, and were unlikely by themselves to lead to any prospect, given the size of the area. I suggested to Peter Hinde that it would be better to convert the remaining obligation to one deep test. Peter recommended this to the operator, who agreed, and the change was approved by the licensing authority.

At this time, Peter Hinde was pursuing his objective of building up an integrated department, and in 1969, the Geology Section was upgraded and accorded the new title of 'Exploration Department'. Peter set about recruiting more explorationists and engineers, but one problem consequent upon our lack of operatorship was that there was little for them to do, other than monitor the various operators' activities. Some new recruits found this lacking in challenge, and said so. Peter, accordingly, looked around for areas in which the Department could become more active. One of these was the provision of well-site geology to the BP/GC well Helpringham No 1 and to some of the Home Oil/BP/GC wells in Yorkshire (e.g. Malton No 1).

Peter at the same time started his campaign for the GC to take over the operatorship of part of the UK onshore area operated by BP. In 1970, he also pushed for the production testing of Wareham No 1. The operator's reported first reaction was 'No, because if it's a poor test it will downgrade the whole basin.' The views on the basin at the time were summed up in the 1971 Work Programme and Budget, in which it was stated that the Jurassic of Dorset showed 'a marked lack of good reservoir rocks.' The reason for this view was largely that Kimmeridge produced from the fractured Cornbrash, and the oil in Wareham was thought to be from the even thinner fractured Inferior Oolite. No predictive model seemed to exist for the development of such fracture porosity. The Triassic Sands were known in Wareham No 1, but no one could think of a way of getting oil into them.

Wareham No 1 was eventually put on pump in November 1970 and produced at 100 BOPD, with increasing water-cut. It produced until 1979, when it was shut in to conserve the energy in an accumulation by then found updip.

In 1972, BP drilled the obligation-satisfying Cranborne No 1, and in the middle of that year Peter Hinde's long campaign for operatorship met with success. It was agreed that the onshore area should be split more or less N-S. In negotiating who operated what, BP elected to take the eastern half, apparently thinking that the East Midlands oil and the Yorkshire gas were better prospects than those uncertain reservoirs in Wessex. Peter gladly opted for the western half, since GC had aspirations in the Channel, with other partners, and the Wessex Basin operatorship seemed to offer the chance to learn more about the offshore. We also got the Cheshire Basin, not dissimilar to the Irish Sea, where we were already operators.

The operatorship was handed over in July 1972, but prior to this I had been thinking that it was about time we knew something about what was going on in the Jurassic. I laid out a series of cross-sections, and with some difficulty had all the disparate logs reduced to 1:5,000, which effectively obliterated most of the lithological information.

This turned out to be a blessing in disguise. One day, I happened to look over the shoulder of a lady colouring in the Wareham No 1 lithology on one of the sections, and noticed that she had coloured only a few sporadic sands at the top of what I could see was about 200 feet of microlog-separation (about half an inch on the section). I asked why she had not coloured in the rest of the sand. She triumphantly produced the 1:500 log and said 'Its not sand, its siltstone, look.' It was only then that it dawned on me that what no-one since 1964 had ever noticed, least of all the man who made this composite log, was that there was a complete contradiction between the lithology as logged, and the microlog beside it (not to mention the SP, it turned out). Such was the persuasive power of the lithological symbols and descriptions. Why the microlog was chosen for illustrative purposes and then conspicuously disregarded remains a mystery. The Bridport Sands on the microlog, in fact, looked like a facsimile of the famous cliff section to the west, with its porous sands separated by tight bands, which become closer together towards the top.

The realisation that the microlog separation proved in a qualitative way the presence of permeability raised the immediate thought that Wareham No 1 might be producing from the Bridport Sands in addition to, or rather than, the Inferior Oolite. The perforations actually straddled the contact. If this were the case, then a structure with more closure could have more Bridport Sand above any OWC. The Bridport Sand could, then, be the missing reservoir in the Jurassic of Dorset.

GC geophysicists had interpreted low fold BP analogue data, and had mapped a structure near a place called Wytch Farm. BP's geophysicists had independently mapped the same structure. As new operators, we had inherited a second well in the 1972 budget and promptly recommended a test of the Bridport Sand prospects at Wytch Farm. I am not sure that we knew it at the time, but we pretty soon found out that in BP's eyes the second well was meant to be a follow-up to Cranborne No 1, which was dry, hence no second well that year.

Nothing loath, we re-recommended the well for 1973, and arrived at the first quarterly technical meeting in the old Ropemaker St. office. The BP Head of Exploration was chairing the meeting. His opening remarks were 'I don't know much about this basin, but what's this Wytch Farm thing you people want to drill?.' Really, it was the same 'Wytch Farm thing' that had been turned down by them the year before.

Eventually, approval was given for a well, provided that it was as cheap as possible. Fortunately, we managed to insist on drilling to a specific Liassic limestone marker, given the obvious difficulty experienced in seeing the sand in the Bridport at Wareham. No mud-logging was allowed by our partner, although we did manage to hire a gas- detector for the well site geologist to operate (of which, more anon). No provision was made for completion of any discovery.

Since we were at last operating our own onshore well, I was issued a pair of 'Redwing' drillers' boots. As I said to Peter Hinde at the time, these boots were the British Gas equivalent of the BNOC company car.

Wytch Farm No 1 was spudded in late 1973, but GC's enthusiasm for operatorship had got a bit out of hand. As a result of the vagaries of rig availability, we found ourselves operating the deep Knutsford No 1 wildcat in the Cheshire Basin at the same time. With only one really experienced well-site geologist (for various reasons), this presented a problem. For reasons that seemed logical at the time, and probably connected with the better known stratigraphy of experienced man on Knutsford. (I well remember spending New Years Eve 1973 on the well-site, instead of with my in-laws the other side of the Mersey, whilst the well-site geologist spent it with his in-laws in Knutsford town. We ground all the diamonds off a core-head, which made for slow progress that particular night.)

The lot then fell on Geoff Reed to sit the Wytch Farm well as his first solo effort, a task not without problems. A cold snap froze the hose-pipe used to wash the samples, a power failure necessitated the use of a flash light to look at samples, and no response of any sort was produced by the gas detector. Worst of all, no Bridport Sand was seen beneath the Inferior Oolite.

Suddenly, high to prognosis, Geoff spotted the Liassic limestone marker to which we had mercifully insisted on drilling. He re-ran the samples and finally saw traces of the very fine Bridport Sand, with oil shows, none of which had been revealed by the gas detector. It later turned out that the pipe leading to the detector was kinked against the wall, and although it worked fine when tested, it received nothing from the mud! The well, incidentally, had gone through a small fault not originally seen on seismic, which shortened the drilled section between the Cornbrash and the Bridport Sand.

The well was logged, and John Bains, GC's log analyst, recalls that the BP expert came with two acolytes, who witnessed the running of the logs. In a preliminary well-site interpretation, John interpreted the Bridport Sand to be oil bearing, but the BP representatives thought it wet. John took the precaution of ordering the taking of sidewall cores, before returning to the hotel to consult the BP guru, who was in bed. He did descend Noel Coward-like in his dressing gown, but also pronounced the Bridport Sand 'wet'. John returned to the well-site, to see the first oil-filled sidewall cores being pulled. The well was eventually tested, and the fact that it was a discovery was leaked to the press by some bar-room expert. The BP Sunbury petrophysicist still insisted to John that it would soon go to water. As far as I am aware it has not done so yet, 20 years later.

As soon as it became obvious that a major oil accumulation had been found, all sorts of interests made themselves known.

The local Planning Authorities soon got in on the act, and raised some early objections. BP sent an expert down from Aberdeen to sort us out in our approach to the planners. The only recommendation I can remember was that he thought that 'we should put the monkey in their ball-park.' (Mixed metaphors are bad enough, but

Fig. 8.3
Wytch Farm from the air.

mixed cliches...really!)

Another objector was the ball-clay industry, a major employer in the area. (Ball-clay is a kaolinitic deposit in the Tertiary, originally sold in 'balls'.) It was pointed out that each of our wells was going to sterilise a huge area of potential ball-clay, which was going to cost us. To find out just exactly how much or how little, we were invited to hire the company's own drilling rig to carry out an extensive sampling programme. Peter Thompsett stopped this little flight of fancy by pointing out that we were thinking of awarding a large seismic contract in the Irish Sea to a British company recently acquired by the parent company English China Clay.

Environmentalists and NIMBY'ists also woke up. A meeting was set up to allay fears, and a mini-bus tour arranged of contentious sites. It is said that no-one used the buses, people preferring to use their own cars to protest about oil exploration. At about this time, one Sunday afternoon I saw an old couple driving their Hillman Avenger through Amersham, Bucks. In the back window they had two stickers. One said 'Say No' to nuclear energy', whilst the other said 'Oil means spoil in Dorset.' I said to my wife, 'I bet they go home, park their car and put on the electric kettle to make tea, without thinking for a second about where it all comes from.' I was also verbally attacked at neighbourhood parties by defenders of England, who had driven there in their foreign cars.

Other problems foreseen by lovers of nature and haters of oil exploration concerned a rare spider, which only lived in old quarries, and an orchid that only grew on road verges, where limestone from the road had raised the pH of the otherwise acid soil. These same verges, onto which our vehicles were expressly forbidden to encroach, were said to be littered with Range Rovers when the hunt was about.

To take the oil to the refinery, it was decided to resurrect the defunct railway line through Furzebrook. Normally regarded as a 'good thing,' this use of rail met with opposition from those playing steam railways at weekends. The tanks at Furzebrook had to be camouflaged and buried behind banks, to render them as near invisible as possible, whilst on the other side of the track was the biggest collection of ramshackle, dusty, corrugated-iron sheds I have ever seen. These belonged to the clay diggers, and had I suppose been abandoned, along with the railway, in a move to road transport.

Later in 1974, GC drilled at sole cost the obligation well on the eastern licences, by redrilling Arreton No 1 on the Isle of Wight, which had stopped just short of the Bridport Sand. In the event, neither oil nor sand was found in Arreton No 2. I think it fair to say that not much thought was given to this, given pressure to develop Wytch Farm, but two Channel partners had given bottom-hole contributions to Arreton No 2. One day in mid 1976, John Fuller of Amoco rang to say, strictly unofficially, that their in-house geochemistry had shown rich, mature source-rocks in the Lias and Kimmeridge of Arreton No 2. Furthermore, the oil sample traded from Wytch Farm was a normal marine Jurassic oil.

All of this geochemistry was somewhat at variance with the BP Sunbury results on the Wytch Farm section and oil, which concluded that no source rocks were found in the Lias (the Kimmeridge is missing), the section was immature, and that Wytch Farm oil had suggestions of a fresh-water origin. The immaturity of the Wytch Farm section is a fact, but the lack of Lias source rock was a sampling problem, and the 'fresh water' source was an over-enthusiastic interpretation of the δC^{13} *data.*

The new observations eventually led the writer to the interpretation that Wytch Farm Bridport Sand oil came from the mature Jurassic section to the south of the Purbeck/Isle of Wight Disturbance, before Alpine inversion. Implicit in this interpretation was the possibility that oil could also have migrated into the Triassic Sherwood Sandstone, on its way to the Bridport Sand. The fact that the Bridport Sand and the source were both Jurassic was neither here nor there.

This was written up, and an expurgated version, giving as little information as possible on Arreton No 2, was sent to BP. The report elicited no reaction, either from above Peter Hinde in GC or from BP, that is until Dave Havard, in 1977, recommended a Triassic test at Wytch Farm. From our own GM, came the reaction to Peter of 'Who says there's oil in the Trias?' Peter said that it was all in Colter's report. 'What report?' was the response. I was then invited to find my report, if I could, anywhere in the GM's office, and spotted it immediately, as the only blue file in a foot-high pile of material.

Similar reactions came from some in BP, although it is fair to say that the Eakring personnel were supportive once they had been given the report. Teeth were finally gritted, however, and a deviated well to the Triassic under the hade of the fault was agreed, despite its uselessness as a Bridport producer in the event of its being dry in the Trias.

Once again, the fact of a discovery was leaked to the press around Christmas 1977.

Somewhere in my garage, I still have a Kilner jar of mud and oil from the first test, given to me by wellsite geologist Peter Bryant. Wytch Farm moved from merely being the largest UK onshore field towards being the largest in a large part of Europe.

The final bit of serendipity that I know of in this story occurred during the drilling of a Trias water-injection well northwards from Goathorn Point. Geophysicists had always swung the fault bounding the next block to the north in a northerly curve, in an area of poor control. In the event it did no such thing, and the 'water injection' well went through it and into the oil-bearing Trias on the northern fault block, thereby just about doubling the known reserves, by confirming a common OWC.

When we came to publish the technical story of Wytch Farm in 1980, I thought that it would not do to rely on bootleg geochemistry from Arreton to explain the Triassic discovery. We therefore sent a Wytch Farm well and Arreton No 2 to a firm of consultants, noting only that they were South England wells. Back came the results with identical maturities in both wells, based on vitrinite reflectance measurements. Telephone discussions and remonstrations that these results were impossible, given the very different burial histories of these two sections, made no headway or impression at all. It is a salutary observation that had we had these results first, rather than the bootleg results, the whole theory that led to the Triassic discovery would not have developed as it did, and probably would not have developed at all at that time.

Reactions closer to home to the Wytch Farm discovery in particular, and to explorationists in general, were hardly more encouraging, as is well illustrated by the following rather bizarre little vignette. During the development of the Bridport Sand accumulation, 5cm plastic cubes saying 'BRITISH GAS, Oil from Wytch Farm, Dorset' began to appear on desks all over 59 Bryanston Street. Apparently, they were also liberally sprinkled around the City of London. They appeared everywhere, that is except in Exploration. I asked one person whose desk was graced by such a cube where it came from. 'From PR Department' was the reply. Accordingly, I rang someone in PR, who confirmed that they existed. I asked if I could have one and was told 'Yes, they are a standard British Gas complimentary item. They cost £2.85' (or thereabouts). I think I told him what he could do with them. Years later, I told this story to Alan Thomas, an analyst in Kitkat Aitken, who was so amazed that he sent me his. So, I got one in the end, without coughing up the £2.85.

In about 1979 or 1980, I was invited to speak about Wytch Farm to the Alberta Society of Petroleum Geologists, in Calgary. Peter Hinde approved with alacrity and I accepted. Peter then had to pass on the request for foreign travel to the Secretariat.

They contacted the GM Exploration Companies, who had no official position in B.G. proper. He was unable to condone such extravagance as an air ticket to Calgary, and I was left feeling, and sounding, stupid as I phoned to say 'I'm sorry, I can't come out to play.'

In early 1981, with privatisation of Wytch Farm and the Gas Showrooms in the air, the union NALGO called a one-day strike to defend the showrooms and their staff. Peter Thompsett and I, who had long accepted the benefits of NALGO's negotiations on our behalf, decided that the only decent thing to do was to go on strike, for the one and only time in our careers, although the showrooms hardly impinged on our corporate or private lives. The craven alternative of taking a day's holiday was rejected by both of us. More than a week later, I was called to stand before the seated Commanding Officer's desk, to be told that he was very disappointed by my behaviour on Tuesday, the week before. Better things were expected of 'The Management Team.' My first thought was to wonder which of my possible indiscretions had caught up with me, having by then forgotten the strike. My look of puzzlement must have betrayed my bad memory, and I was speedily left in no doubt that the strike was the source of displeasure. Being caught somewhat off guard, I could only say that I had not struck for personal gain, but rather to defend the cherished showrooms, which I had only visited about twice in my life. This cut no ice. Peter, who was forewarned by me, had more time to marshal his defence, with no more success. In the end, however, it was Wytch Farm and the other oil assets that went, and the showrooms that stayed, which shows how effective our criticised strike action really was in saving the latter for our employer. If we had struck for Wytch Farm, it might have been saved too.

A post-script to this Wytch Farm exploration success story constitutes perhaps the most significant lesson to emerge. The writer, faced with privatisation of oil assets and the prospect of another decade and a half of the aforementioned management style, fell victim to at least one of the deadly sins, that of pride. It seemed to me that if you can do it in Dorset, you can do it in the East Midlands. In January 1982, I privatised myself by joining Floyd Oil Participations plc, a partner with BP, GC and Candecca in that area.

It depressingly rapidly dawned however, that in all likelihood BP's old-timers, with the tools available to them at the time, had found most, if not all, of the structures in the East Midlands large enough to produce dry oil. OK, so we had better seismic and logs, but it began to seem inescapable that any oil we could produce from the small structures left was not worth the drilling of the other dozen or more dry holes (or wells with good shows and log indications, whose relative permeability characteristics guaranteed they always flowed water.)

Who knows though, maybe someone, some day, will come along and find all the giant strat-traps that those who, over the years, compared the East Midlands with Alberta have always dreamed of. Maybe, also, someone will find the clue to solving the problem of what happened to the oil that was not trapped at Wytch Farm."

Chapter Nine

Data Sharing and the Birth of the PESGB

In previous chapters we have mentioned the paucity of hard data, reference material, and shared experiences to assist oil-finding in these early days. Indeed, the exploration communities centred around London (and, later Aberdeen) which we now take so much for granted, were in their very earliest stages of evolution - and, like all social animals, were looking to group. This was becoming increasingly important given the speed at which events were happening. As Colin Fothergill says:

"It was on the back of the search for gas from 1964 onwards that the PESGB was founded and by the time commercial quantities of oil had been discovered in the UK North Sea the Society was well underway. In fact the PESGB 'sprang' into being at about the same time as the platforms were moving out into the North Sea to start first drilling in late 1964."

Now, while many individuals may justifiably stake their claims to early involvement with the PESGB, one particular individual - Bob Dyk of Hamilton Brothers - was notable for his persistence. By 1964, Peter Walmsley remembers, Bob Dyk had:

"Convinced a number of like-minded explorationists of the need for a professional society to promote the exchange of views and information on the geology and geophysics of the North Sea. The problem was how to achieve this. It was not considered politically expedient to create a UK branch of the AAPG; the Institute of Petroleum showed little interest in the upstream side of the industry and the Geological Society did not concern itself with applied geology.

At a meeting of oil company representatives arranged by Bob Dyk it was concluded that a separate society, the PESGB, should be formed and its objectives were set. The first meeting, to elect officers, was held in December 1964 and, under Bob Dyk's chairmanship, the first technical session was held in January 1965. The initial membership was about 40. From little acorns mighty oak trees grow!"

Bob Dyk himself remembers:

"The only practical solution was to form an exploration society so information could be gathered and shared. So we decided to try and do so. The 'we' was a small group who had been active in American exploration societies and who had worked in foreign exploration. All the companies holding licences were contacted as well as contractors and invited to a meeting to test the water. Some forty people attended the meeting. The problems, as we saw them, were pointed out and the proposed solutions presented.

1) *An organization called 'the Petroleum Exploration Society of Great Britain' would be formed, and Its constitution would be modelled after that of the similar Libyan group.*

2) It would hold monthly meetings to which eminent qualified speakers on the geology of NorthWest Europe would be invited to lecture. This would naturally include candidates from all the countries bordering the North Sea.

3) Membership fees would be minimal so that any working geologist could join. This was in the pre-expense days.

4) The talks would not be published or reported. This would permit speakers to express opinions informally.

5) The Society would never become a publisher because of the costs in doing so.

6) The Society would provide a needed forum for exploration people to meet each other.

7) Officers would change each year with only the past chairman as an ex-officio member of the new council.

It was not an easy concept to sell. The objections were reasonable and constructive. They were less 'national' than those to which I had been subjected before this meeting when I had been lunched and lectured about trying to 'Americanize' the British. The organising group was told to go ahead and a date was set to formally meet and elect officers. This was done in December and the first technical session was held in January 1965."

Colin Fothergill continues:

"During 1965 more geophysicists from overseas came to London and membership of the PESGB provided a unique meeting ground for the geological/geophysical fraternity to meet and exchange information, discuss problems and listen to topics of mutual interest in the lecture programmes. Membership was still small enough for most of us to get to know each other and make long term friendships which were to last many years. Because of the interest in the gas prospects of the southern North Sea technical meetings reflected this in their emphasis on such topics as salt tectonics, developments in seismic techniques and well log interpretation.

Financially, however, the Society was running on a shoestring and as it was the practice to pay the expenses of visiting lecturers a near crisis developed during 1965 when a distinguished geologist from abroad who came to talk about a topical subject brought his wife with him for an extended stay in London, nearly bankrupting the Society. Bob Dyk often used to recount the story, and I suspect, generously met the bill - though he would not admit it!"

He certainly wouldn't, remembering the occasion as follows:

"The Society was never markedly American as many had feared, but strongly international. There were never any problems in getting speakers of international standard; perhaps somewhat helped by the lure of a 'free' evening in London. The cost of hotels and meals was very modest in those days. One evening, however, broke the Society bank. Herr Professor Richter-Bemberg was the acknowledged world expert on the Zechstein. His public appearances were rare. The bait of an evening in London could not be resisted. He arrived from Germany and so did Mrs Richter-Bemberg. They stayed not one night but two. They stayed not in a hotel of our choice but at a luxury one. We willingly paid in full - after all, he attracted a record audience of some 250 and our membership numbers improved substantially. Our completely depleted treasury was rescued by several companies becoming (under some pressure) sustaining members."

However, in the earliest days there were no sustaining members, so every little financial saving was a big help. Colin Fothergill recalls:

"The hospitality of the Geological Society which made its rooms available for meetings at Burlington House was a tremendous help. The Westbury Hotel (used initially) remained a venue for meetings for only a short time and early in 1965 we were able to meet at the Geological Society.

Meanwhile the North Sea Operators' Committee had been formed, again with the active support of Bob Dyk, and this met at the Institute of Petroleum in New Cavendish Street. Most members of NSUKOC were also then members of the PESGB and this enhanced the club-like atmosphere which was so typical of the oil fraternity in London at that time."

But what of the first field trip? He continues:

"Interest in the prospects of the English Channel led the Society to arrange its first field trip to the Devon/Dorset coast in 1965 with Professor Scott Simpson of Exeter University and Geoff Brunstrom of BP as leaders. This was the first of many follow-up excursions to this classic area by the PESGB and others: (see Fig. 9.1).

Fig. 9.1 A lobster lunch at the Picnic Inn, Osmington Mills, Dorset. Photo includes Mike Schmeitzner (Signal); Dick Bannister (Signal); David Pascoe (Superior); Colin Fothergill (RSM); Norman Falcon (BP).

1966 saw Dr Peter Kent, Exploration Manager of BP, as Chairman. His distinguished position at the heart of British geology, and his international reputation were a great asset to the Society. He was later knighted in recognition of his services to petroleum geology and the UK oil industry - one of the few to be so honoured in the history of UK oil exploration. Fig. 9.2 shows him at the head of his 'team' in the PESGB committee of 1966. Committee meetings at that time were usually held in Hamilton's office, hosted by Bob Dyk, and the Committee in 1966 comprised (from left to right in the picture) Fred Kelley (Marathon); Howard Karren, First Vice-Chairman (Monsanto); Paul Biscarrat (Total); Peter Kent, Chairman (BP); Bob Dyk (Hamilton); Jan Winter (Signal); Donald Brown, Second Vice-Chairman (Consultant); Colin Fothergill (Royal School of Mines). Bob Dyk, Peter Kent and Donald Brown are no longer with us and most of the other committee members have left the UK scene. Jan Winter was still involved until quite recently heading Floyd Oil in the UK and I left the Royal School of Mines in 1971 to join Tricentrol which was expanding its North Sea interests. The PESGB was particularly well supported by Signal Oil in the early days. In 1967, for example, Jim Bentley- Llewellyn, Chief Geophysicist of Signal in London became Chairman, and Mike Schmeitzner, then a well-site geologist with Signal, joined the PESGB in 1965. Mike, now Exploration Manager of Svenska in London, is one of the few who have worked in the UK scene without a break for nearly thirty years.

Fig. 9.2
The PESGB Committee of 1966.

Fig. 9.3 Teaching field geology to students - Prof. W. Dan Gill in the Yorkshire Dales, Spring 1966 with D.I.C (now MSc.) Petroleum Geology students.

Membership of the Society increased steadily during 1967 as more companies set up offices in London and those already established increased their technical staff. Again the activities of the Society matched the way in which the pattern of exploration activity was widening. The discovery of oil and gas in Zechstein carbonates by Burmah in 48/22-1 and Signal in 53/4-1 for example raised hopes of finding commercial oilfields in a reef habitat closer inshore than the Rotliegend gas finds, and the Society's second field trip in 1967 concentrated on the Permian Zechstein of the East Midlands. It was led by Dr Denys Smith of the British Geological Society and organised by Ian Forrest, one of our founder members and First Vice-Chairman in 1967.

The PESGB field trip in 1969 was organised by Mike Mason to study the Carboniferous of the Midland Valley of Scotland. Mike will be well known to many members for his long term support of the Society. Between 1967 and 1978 he served on the committee four times, being elected Chairman in 1978."

Peter Walmsley follows on:

"1971 saw us in Scotland again. The trip was memorable for its utterly perfect September weather. It was also memorable for the problems encountered when the party, having driven from Inverness via Brora and Caithness along the north coast to Tongue (near Cape Wrath), arrived at the Ben Loyal Hotel. Thanks to some mix up the 30 or so weary geologists found themselves booked into 15 or so double beds, these being the only rooms available. There was, however, a happy end to the story. The manager of the neighbouring Tongue Hotel, which had closed for the winter, took pity on us and re-opened his very comfortable premises for the night, thereby relieving what could otherwise have been a most interesting situation. Praise be for Scottish hospitality!"

John Church recalls, at about the same time, Robertson Research (now SPT) were beginning their famous field courses which enjoyed many successful years - and clients throughout the industry:

"The first proper field course that Robertson Research ran in 1971 was linked to their first multiclient study and was a disaster. The location was Skye, and Cyril Haskins and myself were only informed that we had been given the 'glorious leader' role when half way up the M-6.

Fig. 9.4
Moray Firth Trip, April 1978.

This inglorious event is firmly fixed in my mind as much because, when in search of one of the Lower Jurassic coral beds in the Broadford area, I had to persuade the participants with 50% success, to remove their boots and wade across a small river. Alas this proved to be a futile exercise since I couldn't find any wretched corals. However, the lesson was learnt and Cyril and I vowed never to lead any future trip without proper preparation, a sentiment which the management responsible for the debacle thankfully accepted. Robertson's soon realised that there was a role for more focused field trips and, with the Middle Jurassic discoveries in the North Viking Graben in mind, arranged the first Yorkshire course under the leadership of Cyril Haskins and Nigel Hancock. This proved to be an outstanding success and encouraged me to look at the Moray Firth and even to return to the scene of our original debacle, the Isle of Skye. The final course of the 'standard four' on which most companies sent their staff was to Devon and Dorset organised and led by Alan Taylor and John Berry,

Fig. 9.4 of a Robertson Research trip to the Moray Firth in April 1978 will hopefully bring back warm memories for some of the Society's members."

It was in the same year as this Tongue field trip that Ken Glennie had his first involvement with the PESGB - a long term affair that began with a telephone call:

"My first contact with the Society was in 1971 when J. C. Van Wagner phoned me in The Hague, to request a talk for early 1972 on Deserts & the Rotliegend (I Can't remember the proper title). In those days, the Geological Society's 'debating chamber' was shaped like the House of Commons with a divided audience facing each other across two sides of a rectangle while the lecturer stood near the 'Speakers Chair'. Shortly after, the PESGB had to find another venue when the old debating chamber was dismantled and the present lecture theatre built.

As an aside, I remember that two geologists from smaller oil companies afterwards made a special point of thanking me for my talk, for up until then, they had had no idea that Rotliegend sediments were the deposits of a desert environment. Company confidentiality obviously worked. The philosophy of my employers, Shell, on divulging research work had been that competitors will know most of your results within about two years of its completion, so after that the Company might as well get some credit for divulging it officially. Up until then, the spread of this particular information within the UK seems to have been very slow despite having had widespread exposure in 1971 during an AAPG lecture tour of the States. Walls had ears, especially in pubs, so people didn't talk to each other.

During the earlier years of the PESGB it was often very difficult to find speakers for the monthly meetings. I remember that only too well from my own stint on the committee (1979), when on at least one occasion the speaker's name was known only a couple of weeks earlier. I think that part of the problem was the obsession of many of those earlier managements, especially during the intense drilling programme of Fourth Round acreage, that something vital to their operations might slip out in error. This seemed to be especially the case with American companies, many of which had to obtain approval from the States before a talk could be given - and as time ticked by, on more than one occasion a refusal was the outcome. They still had not learned from the example set by Myles Bowen of Shell that, in the long run, if each gives a little, everyone gains a much greater sum total of knowledge. But it was coming."

Perhaps the major catalyst needed by the industry to bring about more sharing of ideas and information was provided by the First 'Petroleum Geology of NW Europe' conference held at the Bloomsbury Centre in London in 1974. The PESGB (of course!) was one of the four main organizing bodies, the other three being the Geological Society of London, The Institute of Geological Sciences and the Institute of Petroleum. At this first conference, Leslie Illing recalls:

"A large amount of new and hitherto confidential data was released by the several exploration groups. We have now got used to this more open policy, and the industry as a whole has gained greatly thereby. It was a marked change from the former almost universal secretive policy of oil companies: witness the reported comment of the late Sir Kingsley Dunham that this was "one of the only scientific conferences I have attended where almost everything was new."

Ken Glennie adds:

"So much basic information on North Sea regional and oilfield geology was released by the industry on that occasion, that it has been impossible to match it since. Indeed, if you look at the Foreword to the volume containing the papers presented at that conference (Woodland, 1975), the chairman of the organising committee, James Moorhouse, quoted the comment of a leading geologist as follows: 'This was the most important and significant geological conference ever presented in the European area, and possibly in the world, in view of the great importance of the North Sea development in the total world energy picture.'

Although industry geologists had been using much of their company's newly acquired seismic and well information as their daily bread and butter, little of it was known to other companies and even less to Academia. As an example of this latter situation, I happened to be sitting next to a learned academic during a talk by, I think, one of the Ziegler brothers, in which the broad structure of the Viking Graben had been divulged. After the talk, the professor stressed the importance and quality of some of the information being released by saying that only the previous year he had said to his students 'What stupid people these oil company geologists are, drilling in the middle of the northern North Sea when anyone can see that the Caledonian rocks stretch all the way from Scotland to Norway.' He had just heard that a deep graben separated the two Caledonian areas.

This massive release of geological data, to the benefit of the whole oil industry, was in no small measure due to the activities of Myles Bowen. As chairman of the PESGB during the initial stages of organisation of the conference, and on the planning committee throughout, Myles persuaded other exploration managers that if they had discovered oil or gas, they had nothing to lose and everything to gain by publishing the essential data on reservoir, structural style, and recoverable reserves, He supported this arm-twisting by saying how much Shell would release on field data and on regional studies.

Having set the precedent at the first conference of releasing a useful amount of information in publications on the continental shelf of NW Europe in general, and the North Sea in particular, these began to be a regular feature of geological journals, so that the following three conferences were unable to match the amount and importance of the information released. Even so, there has been no shortage of high-quality papers in the later volumes. Perhaps to suggest that the volume of information released at the later conferences was limited, is wrong. By then, we knew so much more and the impact was not so great. The amount of information released, however, continued to increase from conference to conference as company managements began to realise that they could not afford to be seen failing to contribute. By this time, it was not Myles Bowen doing the arm twisting but John Brooks at the Department of Energy. In terms of amount, the volume of the First Conference has 501 pages with generous margins. The second has 520 pages of smaller print and narrower margins. An explosion to 1200 pages in two volumes for the Third Conference became over 1500 pages, also in two volumes for the Fourth.

Things are now a lot better, not only through the efforts of the successors to the Bloomsbury Conference, but because there has been an almost continuous stream of smaller conferences on particular geological problems or other aspects of the industry. Although many were held in Britain, I think it was the Norwegian Petroleum Society that really led the way with a series of meetings in the 1970's. In more recent years, the Petroleum Group of the Geological Society has initiated many ways of persuading companies to divulge some of their secrets, parts of which now grace some of the series of Special Publications."

Certainly, the industry has moved forward recently with policies of increased openness and a willingness to share new data quicker than in past decades. The PESGB has not been excluded from these benefits and regular lecture attendees will notice an increased frequency of topics such as field case histories, new techniques leading to particular successes, and hard data willingly divulged.

Shortly before Bob Dyk died in 1991 he had the following comments to make about the society which he himself had so successfully chaired for the first time 26 years ago:

"It is pleasing to me to see that over the years the Society has gone from strength to strength and has retained its simple concepts. It is, I believe the largest locally based exploration group in the world, excepting possibly Houston. Congratulations to you all."

Chapter Ten

Where Are We Now?

1. The Oil Industry and Exploration

It is mid 1995, at the time of writing, and 16 years on, at least, from stories recounted in the previous pages. But where **are** we now? There is certainly no shortage of explorationists working in the North Sea today who would hesitate upon such a question, and who would hesitate even further if asked to project such an answer, say, ten years hence. The problem is, (calling upon the ever famous cliché) that 'things ain't what they used to be' and today, given the mature status of many of our basins, it is simply impossible to recreate particular aspects of an explorationist's job satisfaction now lost to a bygone era. Speak at length with anyone fortunate enough to have been around at that time and you'll know what I mean. They'll talk of the tremendous rate of change of knowledge; the rate of change of technology; the thrills of genuine wildcat wells in new basins; the frights, dramas, and impressive developments of early operations; the building up of oil communities, friendships, and societies (the PESGB); and the very real probability of being associated (either through technical skills or just good luck) with a major North Sea oil discovery. Strong, character building (as well as, over the years, wallet-building) stuff, and ripe with enviable experience. Myles Bowen tells us:

"I had a boss in Shell who, if he were to read this, would now be muttering his favourite put-down: 'the hindsight of a moron is always superior to the foresight of a genius.' Well, I will happily plead guilty to being a moron if it allows me to look back at what we have done in the past and learn something. In the late 1950's, in an article in the Scientific American, I was greatly encouraged to read that whereas mathematicians were mentally burnt out in their late twenties, geologists did not peak until their early fifties; the reason given was that geologists have to learn by experience. I would like to think that this is very true. People and corporate bodies in our industry frequently make mistakes and then, instead of looking to see what they can learn from them, just plough ahead and make others."

And there are certainly many lines of evidence which can be used to back up such assertions - even in today's climate, where it appears the average age and experience spread of explorers is getting narrower. I recall, on many occasions, hearing the quotation (originally from Janet Watson?) that 'the best geologist is the one who has seen the most rocks'; and also recall finding widespread industry support for this (particularly from geophysicists, who would rather remember the quote as 'the best geoscientist.................'). John Church underlines this doctrine:

"It has always been accepted that geologists and related colleagues benefit tremendously from studying analogues in the field, although, regrettably, many managers view these events more as rest and recreation rather than education. In addition as the current management philosophy allows more decision makers with non-geological backgrounds to assume control of exploration aspects, then this

attitude will only be strengthened. I hope and believe, however, that we shall be able to reverse this trend in future since too great a reliance on software and hardware is a seriously flawed approach without adequate experience to back it up. A return to the rocks, in order to evaluate the more complex integrated solutions properly, will be shown to be an absolute necessity."

But experience also manifests itself in other related data sources - well logs, seismic, knowledge of old wells, and fields - and a fundamental grasp of the overall tectono-stratigraphic framework of the Greater North Sea. Sometimes the past can return to pleasantly haunt you - as Martin David describes below:

"History has shown that it is important to properly evaluate wells and to understand the prospectivity of the acreage. A number of wells have been drilled and abandoned on features that have subsequently become commercial fields. Examples of such 'sleepers' are:

Field	*Official Discovery Well*	*Original Discovery Well*
McCulloch	*15/24b-3 (1990)*	*15/24-1 (1972)*
Telford	*15/22-11 (1990)*	*15/22-1 (1974)*
Scott	*15/21a-15 (1987)*	*15/22-4 (1984)"*

Myles Bowen also adds:

"A really hard look at existing, often old data can yield amazing results as I believe Enterprise's Nelson discovery amply demonstrated. In that case we developed an exploration concept by working in great detail on an analogy which was the oldest field in the UK sector and then set out to look for another in the same area. We soon identified it, but unfortunately on acreage held by competitors. How Enterprise managed to farmin, obtain a 100 per cent interest and discover (or rediscover) the 440 million barrel Nelson (Fig. 10.1) accumulation is another story.

So have we now seen the last new play? With the large number of plays already found I suppose most people think so, but it will not surprise me if others of importance still crop up, whether as a result of imaginative geological thinking or by serendipity."

And it is this quest for new plays (with no objections to luck, either) which will occupy the minds of UK acreage geoscientists well into the next century - along, of course, with the successful and profitable management of those fields already discovered.

So, approaching the twenty first century, let us (at least in part) answer the question of where we are, and then look perhaps at what we have learned from the past. We are trying to be increasingly innovative, increasingly subtle and clever, but are often finding this comes with a trade off for increased risk. Often our ideas will come with the need for deep, expensive wells - and perhaps a hefty work programme to test

Fig. 10.1
The Nelson platform 1995

these concepts. We are becoming increasingly (of necessity) manipulative of our assets and managing them ever more carefully, often leading to the (new?) multi-disciplined team approach where careful regard to the full exploitation process can work to good effect.

We are employing various computerised tools that help us to reduce some of these risk elements (or at least, help us to believe that we are reducing some of the risks) on prospects that in past decades probably wouldn't have been given a second glance. Indeed, skilful manipulation of these tools seems to be a growing pre-requisite for the explorationist of today. Colin Fothergill notes:

"The range of specialities listed among the present membership shows how

exploration 'technology' has changed radically over the past 30 years. A generation ago in the Sixties explorationists needed to acquire a broad base of experience and knowledge and there were far fewer categories of job description. The day of the gifted all-rounder has long gone and he has been replaced by the Hi-Tech specialist. It was inevitable but perhaps some of the excitement and drama of exploration which we experienced in those first five years has gone too?"

We now have vast volumes of data; 3D seismic surveys are now becoming the norm for North Sea blocks (and 4D is currently the buzz word!) Well densities are ever increasing - currently there have been about 2900 exploration and appraisal wells in the UK North Sea, that is, on average, about 40 square kilometres per well (for licensed acreage - see Figs. 10.2 and 10.3). Oil reserves replacement is on the decline, prices are low, staff are by and large leaner and the whole exploration scenario has changed.

Fig. 10.2
Exploration wells (as of end 1994)

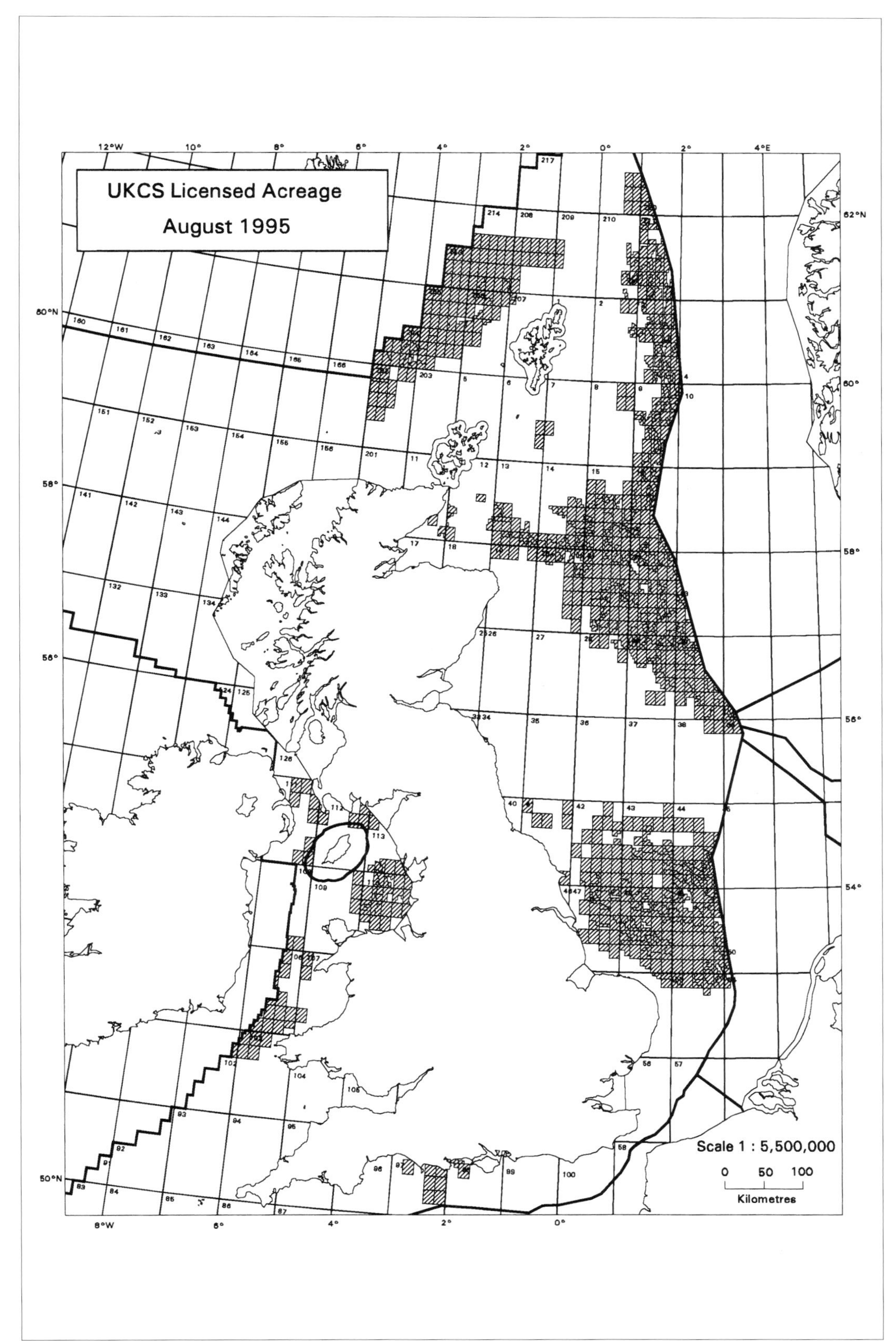

Fig. 10.3
UKCS Licensed Acreage, August 1995

Businesses are more efficient and overall communications have probably improved but, to many individuals, (compared with, say, what they would have been doing 20 years ago) life is more insular. Life is between you and your computer screen, your little patch, eked out by your 'never need another line again' grid of crosslines and inlines and your 'never wonder how this correlates' safety net of tops, logs, and synthetics. Where are we now? Probably working more scientifically, to the very last wiggle, with more data than ever before - but to what avail? (meant in the broadest sense of 'The Greater UK Oil Industry' rather than for the particular fortunes of companies X, Y or Z). We are ultimately chasing a diminishing resource, doing our best, bombarding it with science, but areas left to test new ideas become less and less and the size of what we find, on average, becomes smaller.

So what of our lessons to be learned from the past? Myles Bowen suggests:

"We tended to think too much in terms of layer-cake geology, which worked reasonably in the south but was unsuited to the rift-dominated geology in the north where sedimentary facies changes are the norm. Apart from the general and, in my opinion, undue conservatism of all concerned, I believe that an associated affliction also hinders the efforts of the industry in its efforts to find more hydrocarbons. This is 'bandwagonitis' and geoscientists seem particularly prone to it. It often needs the coining of a buzz-word to set it in motion. For example continental drift never really caught on until it was called plate tectonics (an ugly name); then 'triple junctions' and 'failed arms' were all the rage (although no one seemed to know what caused them), and so on. Another classic was the 'listric' faulting episode in which one company in particular seemed to have issued instructions to all its seismic interpreters to make every fault a listric one. Listric faults have been around for decades, given the required geology, but to try and impose the concept in every situation was absurd. 'Flower structures' are also enjoying a high degree of popularity. In this context it is interesting to note that the once fundamental term 'geosyncline' has disappeared completely from geologists' vocabularies.

If there is one thing you can be sure of in exploration it is that very rarely have you ever got it right. Accepted exploration concepts are probably those that should be questioned most. When an explorer says, 'well of course we know such and such' it is the time to examine whether he really does, or simply thinks he does. Successful explorers have to be sceptical as well as imaginative.

We now have not only one of the most prolific hydrocarbon bearing areas in the world (outside the Middle East) but also one of the most varied in terms of stratigraphy, structure, reservoirs, etc; only the source rocks lack variety, but they certainly make up for it in their prolific production of hydrocarbons and that is what really counts. Here, where a trap has been sourced it is usually full to spill-point; the same cannot be said about many other productive hydrocarbon provinces."

Fig. 10.4 shows our 'present fortune' - those UK fields currently producing (in 1994).

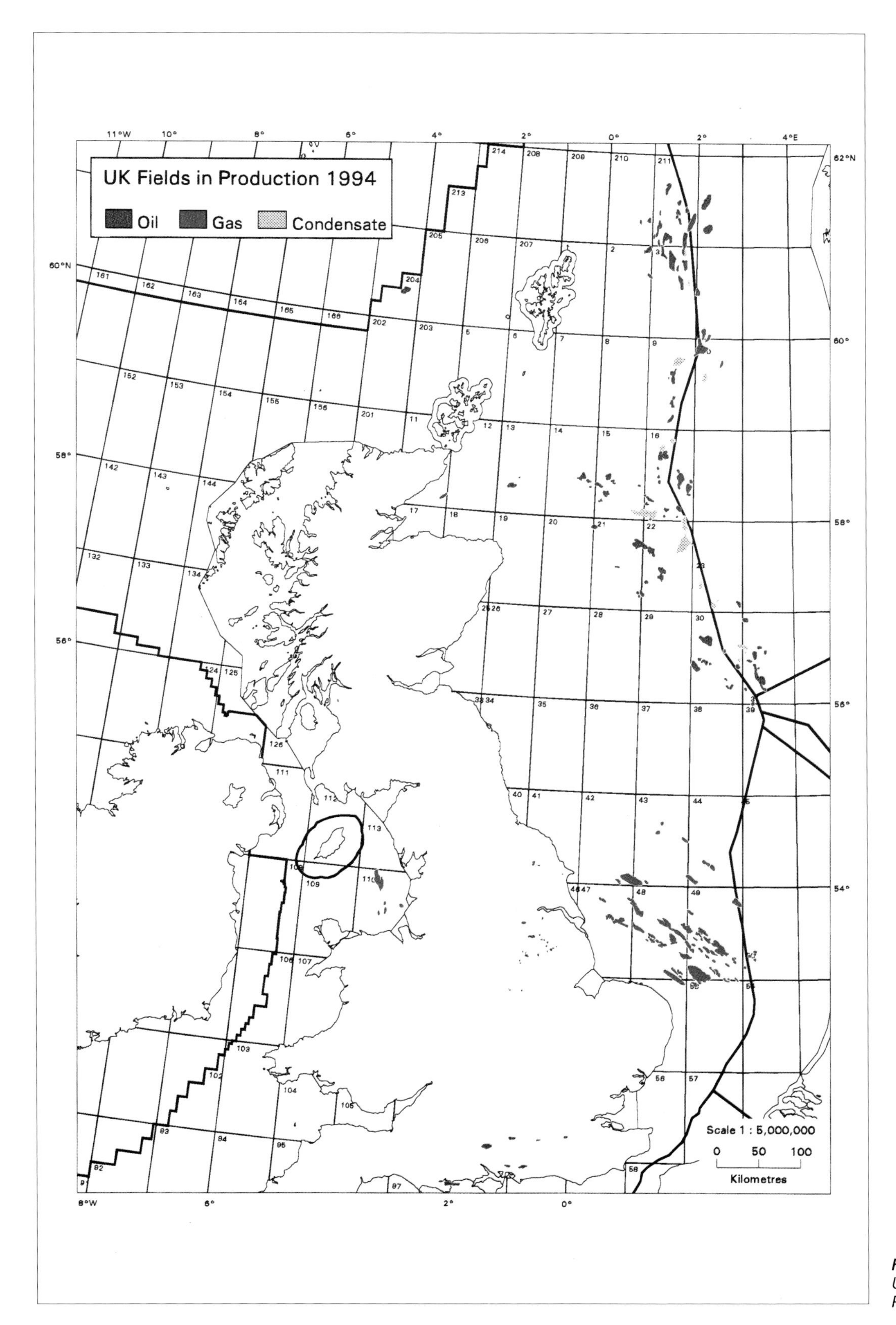

Fig. 10.4
UK Fields in Production 1994

Bob Dyk adds:

"One last word, please. We, in exploration are neglected and forgotten successful professionals except when oil prices are low. Then we - the people who found the oil which is the base on which companies are started and grow - are the first to go. The governments, too, forget us except at tax time. This may not go on forever. I think there is help forthcoming in the newer generations. In late autumn, the primary schools celebrate harvest festival days. The children sing the praises for the Lord's gifts and sing their thank-yous for his bounty. At Christ Church School in Bristol, this verse was once added: 'Deep Beneath the Ocean Floor, Gas and Oil are Laid in Store, Brought to us through Dangerous Toil, Thank you God for North Sea Oil'. Therefore give ye not up hope, there may be a future future!!"

But perhaps the final comment should come from Martin David:

"Since I joined the industry it has often been said that 'most of the North Sea oil has already been found.' It is evident however, that if you stop looking for the remaining oil, then you will certainly never find it."

2. **The Oil Industry and You**

Our business today is leaner, meaner, and probably fitter (depending on your definitions) than ever before, but at what cost (in human terms) has this been achieved? In some respects this is difficult to answer, as the process of slimming down and streamlining by a number of our major companies has simultaneously opened up new opportunities elsewhere - particularly in the field of high technology, geoscience consultancies - but a gap still remains (and the size is hard to gauge) between jobs lost and jobs created. The prospect of future unemployment is a real threat to many workers (and not only geoscientists) in today's carefully risk controlled, cost controlled and high technology North Sea environment.

Dr. Colin Campbell, in a special lecture to the PESGB in early 1994, had this to say when he spoke of 'The End of An Era - What Now':

"In a long historical perspective the oil age is a fleeting one when Mankind burns up the world's recoverable resources formed over eons of geological time. The span of the oil age is now becoming known with virtually all prolific provinces already found. It falls into three epochs: a Period of Growth from its birth to 1970; a Period of Transition from 1970 to 2000; and a Period of Decline from 2000 to its end.

With an ultimate recovery of about 1800 billion barrels (discounting spurious reserve reports) the world approaches the Midpoint of Depletion when rising production gives way to decline.

Probably less than 250 billion barrels remain to be found over about 50 years. Not more than 10 billion are being found a year on a falling trend, whereas consumption stands at 22 billion and rising. The Remaining Oil (Ultimate less Cumulative Production) is most unevenly distributed, much lying in six Middle Eastern countries closed to western oil companies.

The exploration community is being massacred; for the individual it is a devastating experience to have to find a mid-life new career. Should he hang on for better times or bite the bullet?

Current oil prices are grossly anomalous. They are set by the Futures Market, a paper market reflecting the competitive judgement of short-term traders at their screens. They are also influenced by the US grip on Saudi Arabia with low oil price being the quid pro quo for 'defense', and are depressed by the perceived threat of the pending end to the Iraqi embargo. Today's prices reflect depreciated past discovery and fall far below replacement or substitution costs.

But with the share of world supply coming from six Middle East swing producers likely to pass 30% within a few years, the scene is set for another price shock. In fact the ending of the embargo implies agreement between the swing producers: any agreement may trigger the shock.

The consequence may be a final tax-driven boom in exploration and a shortage of survivors from the exploration massacre. But the general inflection from rising to falling production means a fundamental change for the industry. The major international companies are likely to retreat into a dwindling refining and marketing business buying their crude from governments. Independents may thrive, exploiting niches in finding and developing small fields in existing provinces. Lean contractors and 'virtual corporations' (shifting consultant groups) may come into their own, partly working for governments. Gas production and hence exploration for it will grow, but mainly for not very profitable local markets. Production geologists and geophysicists will be in demand everywhere.

The days of the fat cat frontier explorer are almost over, but more pedestrian productionists can expect to earn a modest living worldwide much like mining geologists do.

Advice: stay technical, shun promotion, be accommodating and don't turn down any good offers in banking."

Strong stuff, with which you may or may not agree (depending, among other things, on your love of banking!) but certainly, the fact remains that as a growth industry in the long-term future we're not a very good bet; our product is disappearing.

So how are the explorers of the future coming to terms with the oil industry of today? To what extent do they have the confidence to join our business (thriving richly in the

North Sea at about the time they were conceived)? To what extent do we give them the opportunities to join?

Recent statistics (compiled in 1992 by Andrew Bottomley, Director of the University of Reading's Career Service) suggest that for graduate geoscientists, future openings are still being created - although they are enhanced significantly by postgraduate qualifications. Tables 10.1 to 10.4 illustrate the statistics - compiled from institutions (Universities and Colleges) across the UK. It can be seen that, for first degree geoscientists in oil-industry related employment, service companies (particularly geophysical contractors) offer the most promising openings. For PhD students the situation is reversed, with oil companies gaining most of those interested in joining the industry. Andrew Bottomley comments:

"Many finalists regarded postgraduate study as a short term option to jobs, a path that seems to be confirmed as viable for geoscientists when the proportions of first degree and higher degree holders entering geologically related work are compared.

It is encouraging to observe that of the proportion starting jobs, very few postgraduates were unable to, or chose not to gain geologically related employment - only 11 masters graduates and nine PhDs were in this category and were evenly distributed across the public sector, industry, commerce and temporary work.

In all cases information relates to the status of individuals at 31 December 1992."

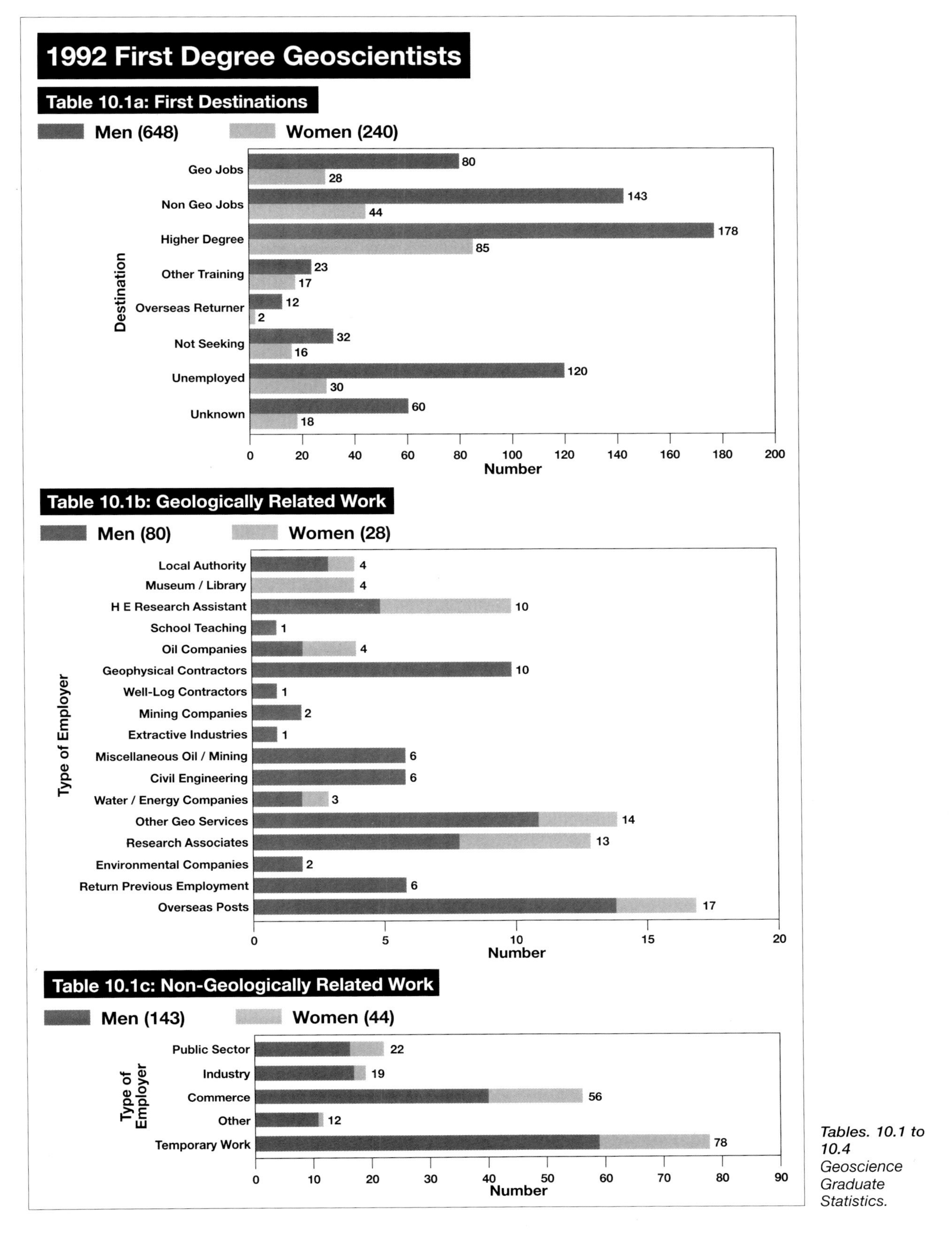

Tables. 10.1 to 10.4
Geoscience Graduate Statistics.

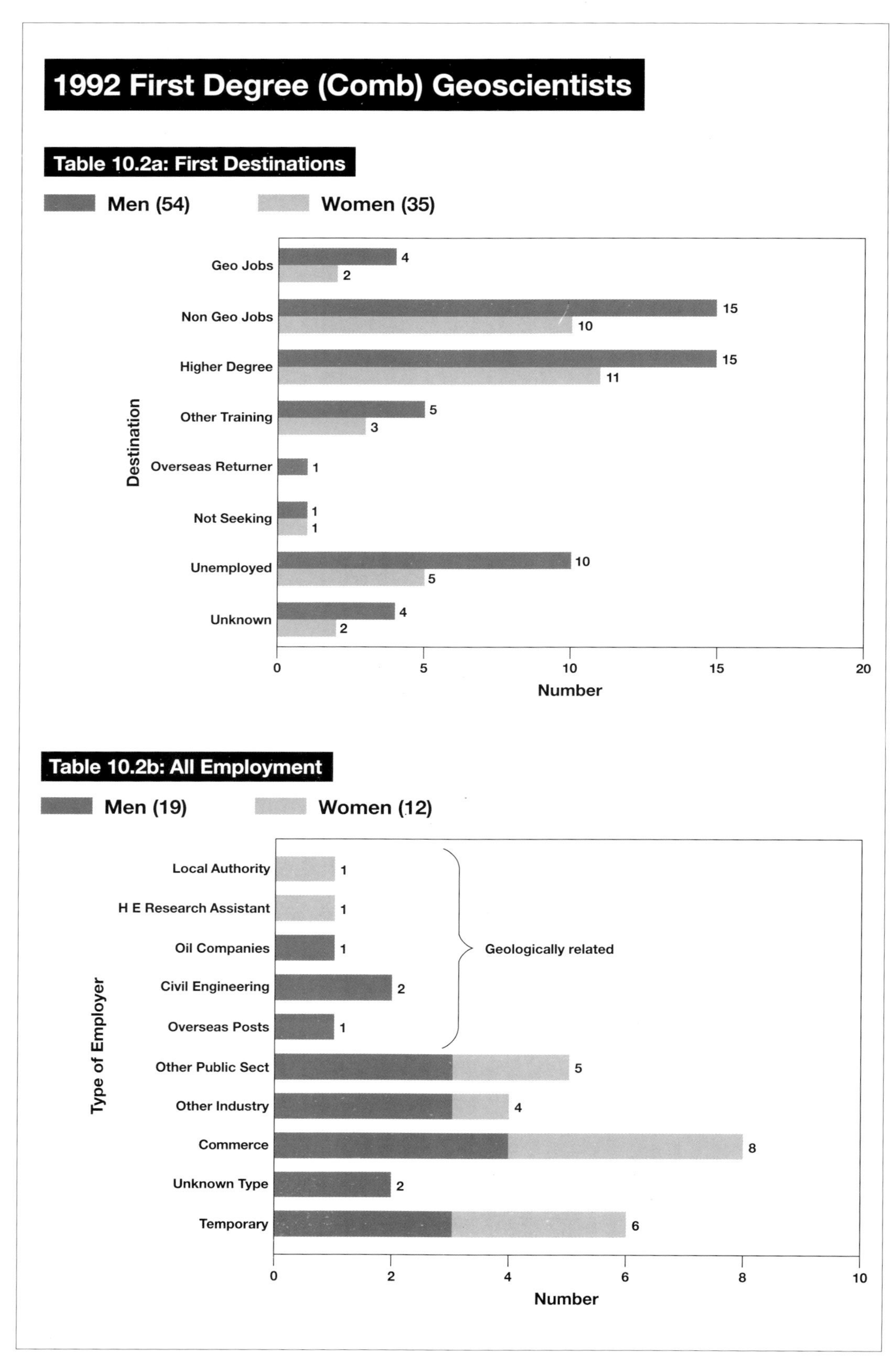

Tables. 10.1 to 10.4 Geoscience Graduate Statistics.

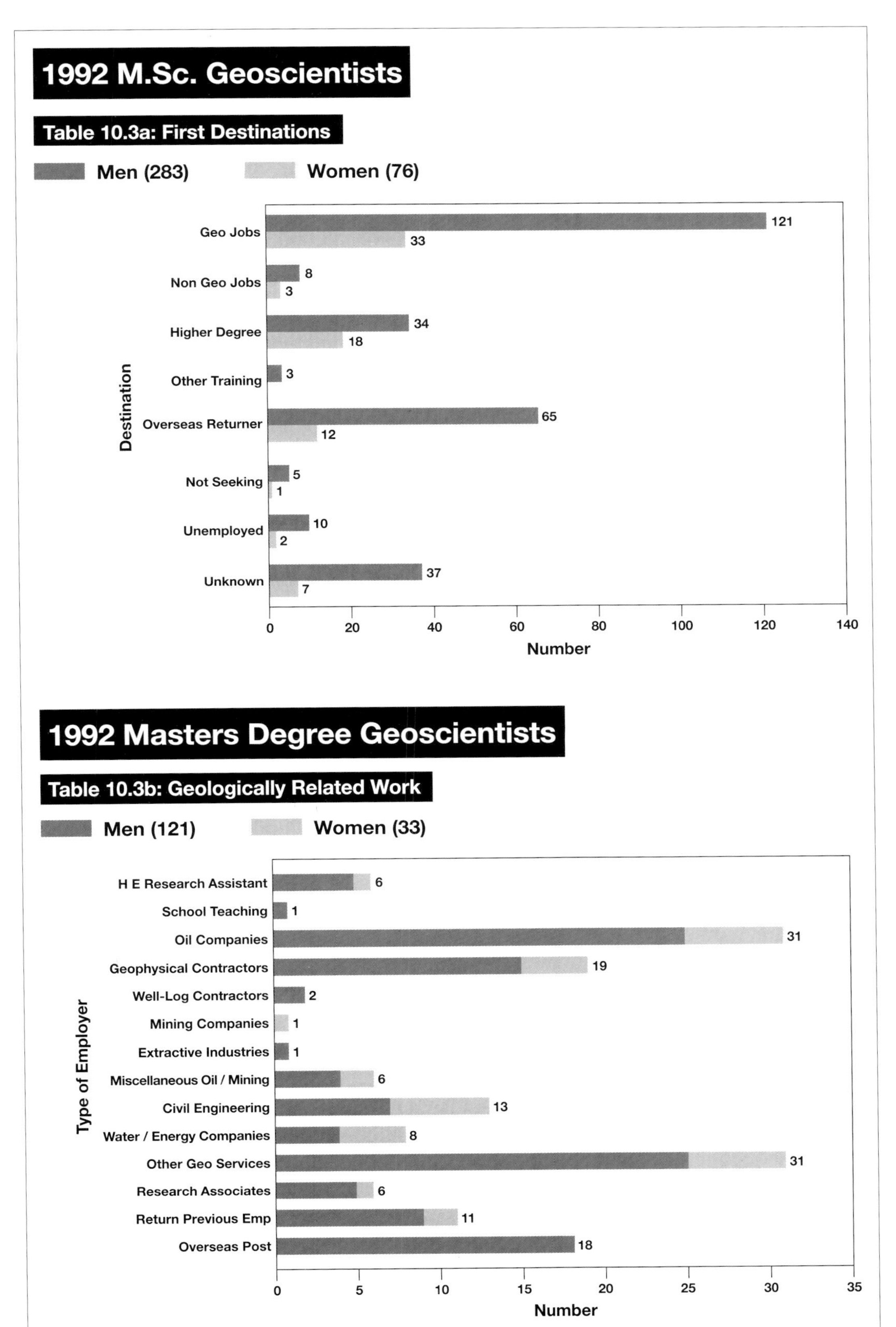

Tables. 10.1 to 10.4 Geoscience Graduate Statistics.

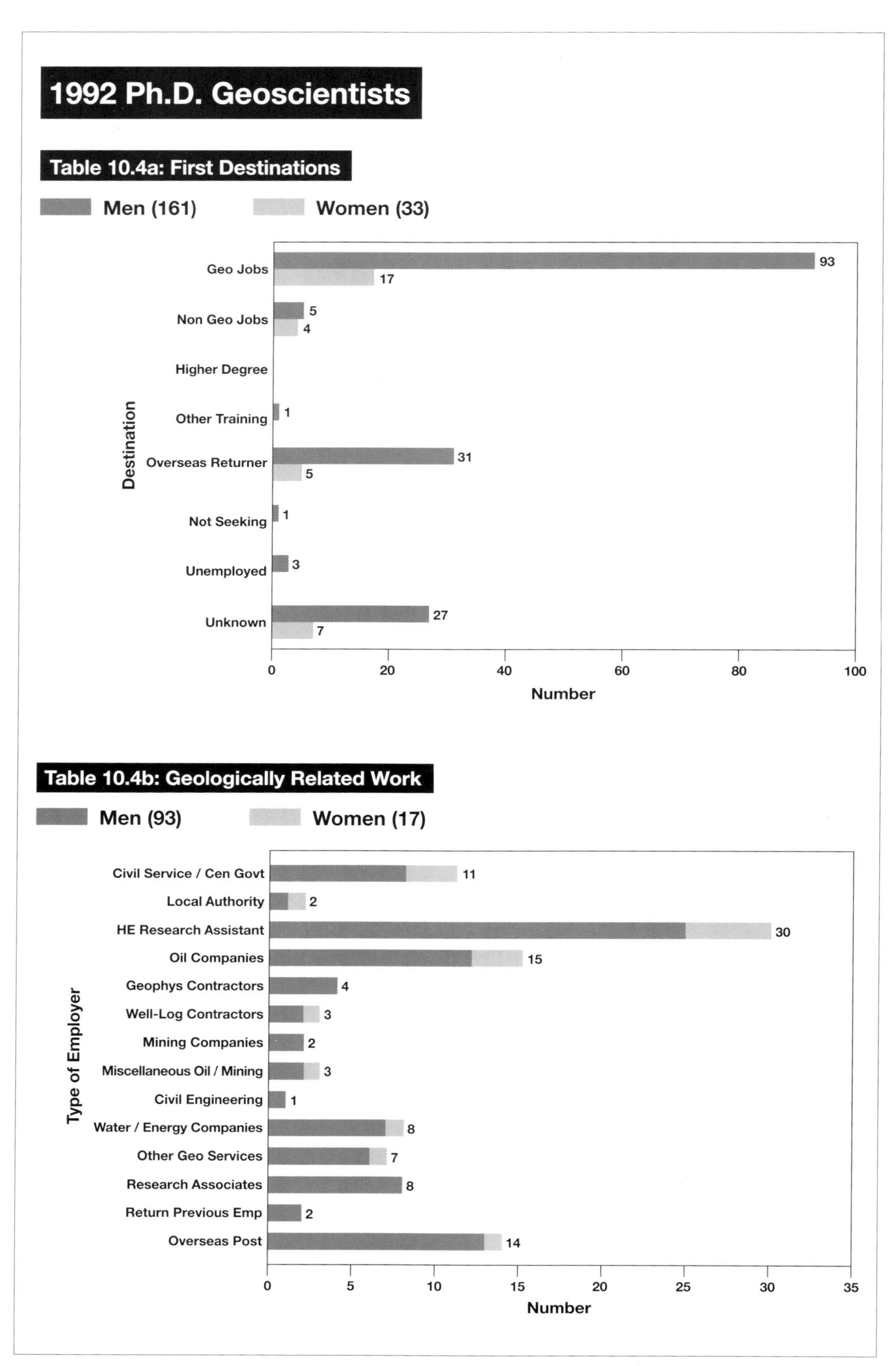

Tables. 10.1 to 10.4 Geoscience Graduate Statistics.

Further encouraging statistics were compiled by the PESGB recently, for a special seminar on careers in March 1994. Questions on exploration staffing levels past, present and future were sent to 62 oil companies and 264 service companies. Response rates were 47% and 15% respectively. Some of the results are shown in Fig. 10.5 which overall suggest we should perhaps be increasingly optimistic about the future.

About a third of the major oil companies claimed not to be streamlining and, even considering those that were, the average exploration staffing levels were not expected to reduce significantly (see Fig. 10.1). Of the smaller companies, only 5% claimed they were streamlining (presumably reflecting pre-existing leanness anyway) and, encouragingly, only 10% of service companies claimed job reductions were on the cards.

If these statistics can be believed (and some of the samples, particularly from the Majors, were quite small), it is possible that new job opportunities created via high tech problem-specific consultancies may go a considerable distance towards counter-balancing the drops in numbers within the larger organisations. We remain shrouded with unknowns, opinions are diverse, much depends on oil price and government policy - but the UK has still a long way to go yet.

If in doubt, consider the announcement of the sixteenth bidding round in November 1994, 30 years on from that very First Round so fondly remembered in earlier chapters. You might think that after 15 rounds of cherry picking, seismic, drilling, relinquishment, awards, more seismic and more drilling, that the stones unturned get fewer and fewer. Charles Wardle, Parliamentary Under Secretary of State for Industry and Energy announced the following:

"I have decided to offer 164 blocks for licensing, an optimum number to enable companies to consider all options in a wide range of different areas. I expect applicants to be committed to the future of the UK Continental Shelf by being competitive, innovative and continuing to cut costs. The largest proportion of the blocks (over 60) are to be West of the Shetlands where I want to encourage companies to build on the impetus of the Foinaven announcement earlier this month. This area has the potential for further significant discoveries and to develop into an exciting new oil province.

The objective of the Round, as of previous rounds, is to encourage exploration - particularly in new areas where there has been little drilling to date - and to continue the development of our oil and gas resources well into the next century. I want the present momentum to be maintained, so I am calling for nominations from companies for the next Round, the 17th, which will cover frontier areas to the far west of Britain where there has been little exploration so far.

Blocks offered in the 16th Round include relatively new basins such as Cardigan Bay

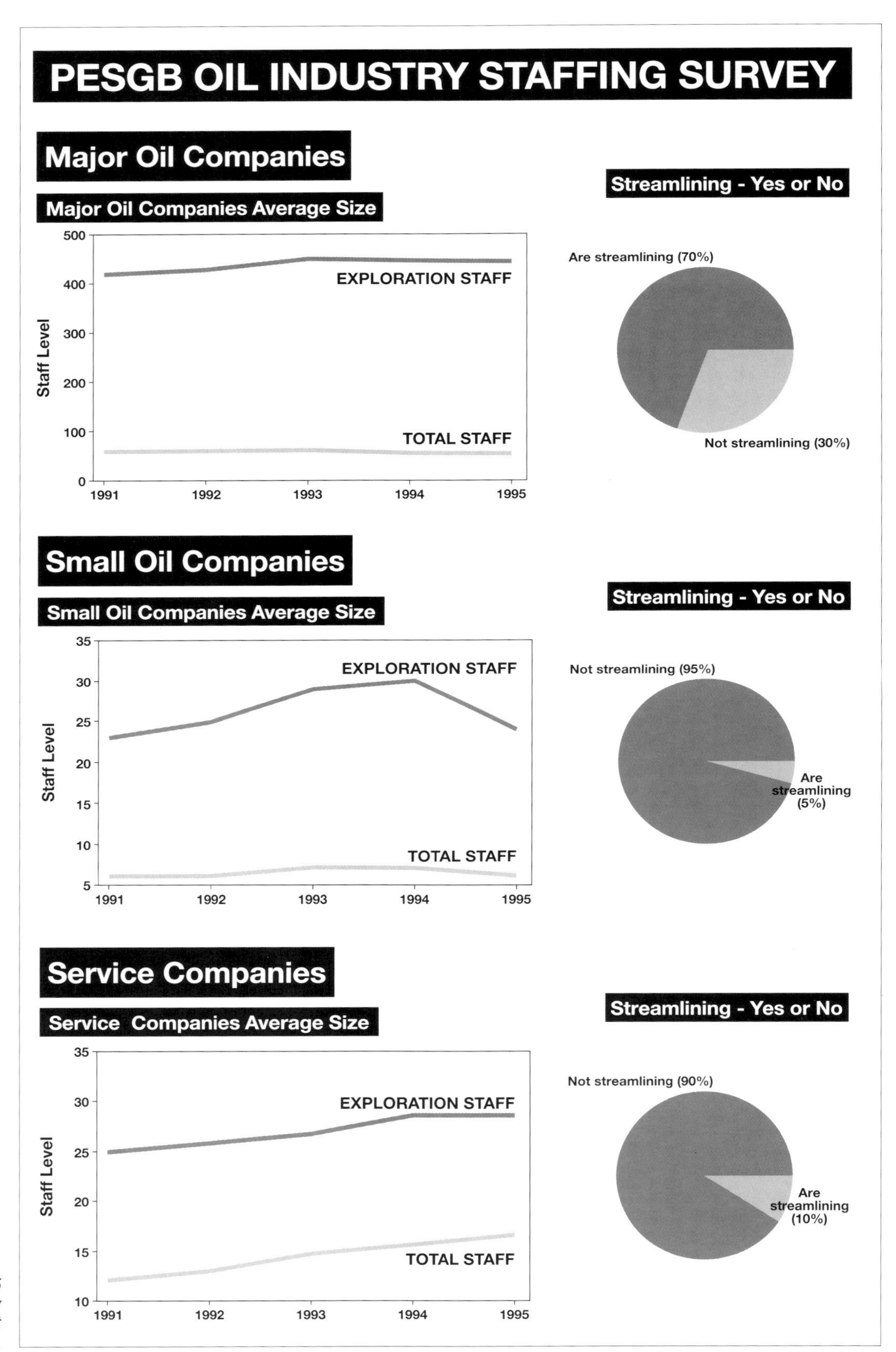

Fig. 10.5 Oil industry employment statistics.

and the East Irish Sea, and in the English Channel, as well as on the fringes of the more established areas of the North Sea. The range of blocks offered illustrates the diversity of opportunities available on the UKCS."

At the time of writing the results from this Round had just been announced, with over 45 groups of companies making bids. In the West of Shetlands area alone there were up to 8 applications for a single block, indicating that even now there is sufficient stimulus and challenge left to generate, at least in part, some of that key elusive exploration ingredient of decades gone by.

3. The PESGB

So where is the PESGB now? From those first meetings at the Westbury Hotel (Fig. 10.6) with Bob Dyk, where have we progressed to in 1995?

Fig 10.6
The Westbury Hotel pictured in 1966

Karen Whitehead, PESGB Administrative Director, provides the following account of where we are today:

"The PESGB currently stands at 4,000 individual members - about a hundred - fold increase from the original 40 or so founders. Membership categories were expanded in the last five years to include associate and student categories, which are growing, although we now appear fairly stable at the 4,000 level. Sustaining members continue to support the Society and its objectives, but have decreased in numbers with the takeover and merging of many companies in recent years.

Today the PESGB is a registered charity, with a subsidiary trading company PETEX Ltd. In 1987 we became registered as a charity with the Charity Commission, the culmination of many years liaison with the Charity Commission and ongoing work on behalf of various Committees. This change meant that the PESGB, always a non-profit making body, was now officially recognised as such, with related financial benefits, such as the claiming of subscriptions against income tax. The objectives of the Society were amended to specify that its aim is to 'promote, for the public benefit, education in the scientific and technical aspects of petroleum exploration.' PETEX Ltd was set up in 1991, as a wholly owned subsidiary company of the PESGB, to organise the bi-annual conference and exhibition. These Exhibitions are now established as the largest UK Technology events, with around 100 exhibitors, over 2,000 delegates, and lectures and posters.

Our most popular event in the year is the Chairman's Evening - the current venue being the Imperial War Museum - which attracted about 1000 members last year and was filmed by the BBC and featured on TV! Sadly, the Christmas party in its previous format could be no more with charitable status, and so the Chairman's Evening as a fundraiser was initiated, but has proved even more popular in various venues from the Commonwealth Institute (with limbo dancing and fire eating and steel bands) to the Museum of London (with 'olde' English food and mead and fancy dress) and dining with the Dinosaurs at the Natural History Museum. Never a dull moment!!

Monthly lectures have continued to be popular, and are held in both London and Aberdeen. The Aberdeen section was initiated some ten years ago, and currently has some 500 members, with its own newsletter, monthly lectures, social events and field trips.

Field trips are run regularly, with a series of over 40 guide books sold at non-profit making rates. Weekend and one day field trips in the UK are usually well attended, but sadly overseas trips have declined in popularity and have not been run for several years. A trip is currently planned to Northern Ireland, and perhaps the PESGB will even venture through the 'Chunnel' to France? More social-oriented building stone field trips have proved popular with members and guests, as have other informal events such as buffet lunches and summer wine tastings. Occasional

Fig 10.7 Examples of PESGB activities.

core workshops have proved extremely popular, and more are planned.

The PESGB holds other seminars and conferences - such as our wellsite operations seminar and environmental conference. We also sponsor and organise other conferences jointly with other societies, such as the Petroleum Geology of North West Europe Conferences - the next one planned for 1997. Links are maintained with other societies, and the PESGB is affiliated to the AAPG, SEG, and EAPG.

The newsletter is currently a monthly 80+ page glossy, colour magazine, packed full of UKCS, NWE and International news, membership information, reports, and articles, with recruitment and technical advertising. Who could have envisaged its growth from a couple of A4 sheets stapled in the corner? This is the main means of communication throughout the Society and input from members via letters and written or verbal news items is always welcomed. We have produced various leaflets, a video, and a Structural Framework Map of the North Sea. The membership directory is updated and distributed annually and has been expanded to include email numbers and direct dial telephone numbers.

Regular questionnaires are held to ensure the Society is still in touch with members' requirements, and from these PETEX was initiated; core workshops were introduced and the newsletter was expanded. Comments and suggestions are always encouraged at monthly committee meetings, and are considered and pursued where possible. For example, letters and comments from unemployed members led to the Society holding regular Career Seminars and producing an initial career guide, now replaced with the current Career Video. Currently, free practical training is being offered to the unemployed. Our annual dues are currently just £20, covering the monthly newsletter, directory, free entry into the monthly meetings in London and Aberdeen, and occasional maps.

Thirty years ago, international explorers came to the UK and shared their experience in exploring for oil in the North Sea and founded the PESGB. Now, North Sea explorers have taken their expertise into international exploration in areas such as Russia, Eastern Europe and Africa, with currently half of the membership exploring for oil internationally, mainly out of London based companies. Our magazine now includes international news and the Society holds Farmin/Farmout seminars for international ventures, and this year is holding a Venezuelan Seminar to tie in with the Licence Round.

Fig. 10.8 *The PESGB committee/book committee members of 1995. From left to right: Norman Hempstead (PESGB Book Committee member), Ray Bate (PESGB Newsletter Director 1995), Richard Moreton (Book Editor), Paul Sandford (Book Committee member and PESGB Secretary 1995), Karen Whitehead (PESGB Administrative Director), John Church (Book Committee member and PESGB Field Trip Director 1995), Rosemary Johnson Sabine (Book Committee member and PESGB Past Chairman 1995), Ian Forrest (Book Committee member)*

Where are we now?

Well, the PESGB is still very much a Society run by its members, for its members.

It now has its own premises and staff, managing to be voluntarily run by an elected committee up until 1984, with c.1,500 members! Paid staff have eased the burden on volunteers, and enabled the Society to increase both the range and quality of its services - but it cannot function without the tremendous support and hard work of individual volunteers (such as the committee members who have produced this book), and the overall backing of companies and the industry as a whole."

Epilogue

A seagull cried
And defiantly rose from the shingle
Exploring, head darting - blatantly mocking
Then fleetingly upwards
Casting but a thin, fading shadow
On the waters below.

But for whom was the dream?
For what vast, defiled subterranean prey do they now weep
Whose precious tears were forcibly shed?
What intricate, interwoven earth-wrenched tombs
Have we opened, laid bare and bled?

(Like a drill)
A sharp, defiant orange beak swiftly dives for food,
Too sure to dream, too driven by circumstance;
He misses - still, he'll try again
No major unknown or risk

Just the spreading ripples

From a peaceful ocean...

Dissipating with time

RAM '95